# CHES® Exam Review

**Elizabeth M. Felter, DrPH, MCHES®**, is an assistant professor in the Department of Behavioral and Community Health Sciences in the School of Public Health at the University of Pittsburgh. Dr. Felter is also an affiliated faculty in the Evaluation Institute for Public Health and the Center for Health Equity. Her teaching, research, and practice foci are in the areas of health and risk communication and evaluation. Dr. Felter holds a BA in English from the College of Wooster, an MA from the University of Georgia in Health Promotion and Behavior, and a DrPH from the University of Pittsburgh. She has been a certified health education specialist (CHES) since 2001 and a master certified health education specialist (MCHES) since 2011.

**Jason D. Flatt, PhD, MPH, MCHES®**, is an assistant professor in the Department of Social and Behavioral Health in the School of Public Health at the University of Nevada, Las Vegas (UNLV). His research program focuses on dementia risk and prevention with vulnerable populations, including older racial and ethnic minorities and LGBTQIA+ adults. He teaches courses at UNLV on community-based participatory research, social and behaviorial health theories, and health promotion practice. He received his BS from the University of Florida College of Health and Human Performance, an MPH from the University of South Carolina Arnold School of Public Health, and a PhD in behavioral and community health sciences from the University of Pittsburgh, School of Public Health. He has been a certified health education specialist (CHES) since 2004 and a master certified health education specialist (MCHES) since 2011.

# CHES® Exam Review

*Certification Guide for
Health Education Specialists*

SECOND EDITION

Elizabeth M. Felter, DrPH, MCHES®

Jason D. Flatt, PhD, MPH, MCHES®

 SPRINGER PUBLISHING

Springer Publishing Company, LLC
11 West 42nd Street, New York, NY 10036
www.springerpub.com
connect.springerpub.com/

*Acquisitions Editor*: David D'Addona
*Compositor*: diacriTech

*ISBN*: 9780826136275
*ebook ISBN*: 9780826136282
*DOI*: 10.1891/9780826136282

22 23 24 25/ 5 4 3 2 1

The author and the publisher of this Work have made every effort to use sources believed to be reliable to provide information that is accurate and compatible with the standards generally accepted at the time of publication. Because medical science is continually advancing, our knowledge base continues to expand. Therefore, as new information becomes available, changes in procedures become necessary. We recommend that the reader always consult current research and specific institutional policies before performing any clinical procedure or delivering any medication. The author and publisher shall not be liable for any special, consequential, or exemplary damages resulting, in whole or in part, from the readers' use of, or reliance on, the information contained in this book. The publisher has no responsibility for the persistence or accuracy of URLs for external or third-party Internet websites referred to in this publication and does not guarantee that any content on such websites is, or will remain, accurate or appropriate.

CHES® and the Areas of Responsibility, Competencies, and Sub-competencies for health education specialists are registered trademark and copyright of the National Commission for Health Education Credentialing, Inc. (NCHEC). NCHEC does not endorse or approve this resource, nor do they have a proprietary relationship with Springer Publishing Company.

**Library of Congress Control Number: 2022910085**

*Publisher's Note:* **New and used products purchased from third-party sellers are not guaranteed for quality, authenticity, or access to any included digital components.**

Printed in the United States of America by Hatteras, Inc.

*This book is dedicated to Robert Kyle and Eleanor Rose.*

# Contents

# Preface

Welcome to the 2nd Edition of the CHES® Exam Review! We published the first edition in 2019 to provide those wishing to take the CHES® exam with additional study material based on our experiences as working health education specialists and public health educators. In 2020, the National Commission for Health Education Credentialing, Inc.[1] (NCHEC) and the Society for Public Health Education (SOPHE) released *A Competency-Based Framework for Health Education Specialists – 2020*. This latest framework identifies 35 Competencies arranged in eight Areas of Responsibility.

Within this guide you will find updated information reflecting the 2020 Framework. We've added an additional chapter to accommodate the eighth Area of Responsibility, which unifies the competencies for Ethics and Professionalism. The practice exam is updated to reflect the new proportion of test questions from each Area of Responsibility, and we've updated the text throughout to reflect best practices within the field. We've added 20 additional practice questions bringing the total to 325 practice questions. We hope you find this a helpful addition to your preparation for the CHES® exam!

---

[1]CHES® and the Areas of Responsibility, Competencies, and Sub-competencies for health education specialists are registered trademark and copyright of the National Commission for Health Education Credentialing, Inc. (NCHEC). NCHEC does not endorse or approve this resource, nor do they have a proprietary relationship with Springer Publishing Company.

# Acknowledgments

This book would not have been possible without the help of many people. We are grateful to Dr. Patricia Documét and Dr. Steve Albert of the Department of Behavioral and Community Sciences and Ms. Linda Duchak and the Center for Public Health Practice at the University of Pittsburgh for contributing questions for the guide. We would also like to thank Mr. Mike Dolinger, at the School of Public Health at the University of Pittsburgh, for his contributions in Chapter 11. Finally, eternal gratitude to Dr. Beth Madison and Dr. Carol Christen; without them this book would not have been possible.

# Pass Guarantee

If you use this resource to prepare for your exam and you do not pass, you may return it for a refund of your full purchase price, excluding tax, shipping, and handling. To receive a refund, return your product along with a copy of your original receipt and exam score report. Product must be returned and received within 180 days of the original purchase date; one offer per person and address. Refunds will be issued within 8 weeks from acceptance and approval. This offer is valid for U.S. residents only; void where prohibited. To begin the process, please contact customer service at CS@springerpub.com.

# So You Want to Take the CHES® Exam?

## ▶ INTRODUCTION

In this chapter, we talk about the things you need to know before you take the Certified Health Education Specialist (CHES®) exam. First, we briefly explain the CHES® credential. Second, we go over who is eligible for the CHES® exam and how you can confirm with the National Commission for Health Education Credentialing, Inc. (NCHEC) that you are eligible to sit the exam. Then we walk you through the process of applying for the exam. Finally, we describe what the day of the exam will be like, what to expect, and give you some strategies to make sure it goes as smoothly as possible.

Much of the information in this chapter comes from NCHEC's website (www.nchec.org) at the time of publication, and our personal experience guiding students through the process. However, procedures can and do change, so always check with NCHEC for the latest information!

## ▶ A BRIEF REVIEW OF THE CHES® CREDENTIAL

Chances are, if you are reading this guide, you already have some idea about the CHES® credential. So if you feel you are already knowledgeable in this area, feel free to skip ahead! But maybe someone just said to you, "You should really take the CHES® exam," or you have noticed that many of the jobs you want to apply for say "CHES® preferred" and you want to learn a bit more. So let us start at the beginning.

In 1978, the National Task Force on the Preparation & Practice of Health Educators was established and over the next decade it worked to develop and promote the Framework for the Development of Competency-Based Curricula for Entry Level Health Educators. Ten years later, in 1988, it became a nonprofit organization, the NCHEC—the name it retains today. In 1990, they administered the first CHES® exam, and 8 years later they began offering the exam twice yearly, as it remains today. In 2008, the credential was accredited by the National Commission on Certifying Agencies (NCCA), and it was reaccredited in 2013. In 2011, NCHEC began offering the Master Certified Health Education Specialist (MCHES®) credential for advanced-level practitioners. We talk more about the MCHES® in Chapter 11.

So, that is the history. But what is a CHES®, exactly? The CHES® credential identifies you as a Certified Health Education Specialist.[1] That means you have been certified by NCHEC as a health educator. But then, what is a **health educator**?

---

[1] A word about terminology: NCHEC uses the term *health education specialist*, and the Bureau of Labor Statistics (and others) use the term *health educator*. We will use the terms interchangeably in this book.

O*Net Online (2021) defines **health education specialists** as those who "provide and manage health education programs that help individuals, families, and their communities maximize and maintain healthy lifestyles." They use data to identify community needs prior to planning, implementing, monitoring, and evaluating programs designed to encourage healthy lifestyles, policies, and environments. Health education specialists may link health systems, health providers, insurers, and patients to address individual and population health needs; may serve as a resource to assist individuals, other health professionals, or the community; and may administer fiscal resources for health education programs.

According to a U.S. Department of Labor (DOL) report in June 2021:

- There were an estimated 62,200 health educators working in the United States.
- Employment opportunities for health educators were projected to grow by 11% from 2019 to 2029, "much faster" than the average for all occupations.
- Nearly half of health educators work in healthcare or governmental organizations.
- Approximately 24% of health educators work in the government sector.

## ▶ CHES® EXAM ELIGIBILITY

Before proceeding further, it is crucial to ascertain if you are eligible to take the CHES® exam. There are two basic requirements to be accepted to take the examination: (a) You must hold at least a bachelor's degree from an accredited institution of higher education, and (b) you must submit an official academic transcript to NCHEC that shows you majored in some form of health education.

*But wait—my degree doesn't say that!*

Do not panic! NCHEC will also accept an official transcript that reflects at least 25 semester hours or 37 quarter hours of course work (with a grade of "C" or better) with specific preparation addressing the Eight Areas of Responsibility for Health Education Specialists.

## ▶ WHAT ARE THE EIGHT AREAS OF RESPONSIBILITY FOR HEALTH EDUCATION SPECIALISTS?

We are glad you asked. These are important to understand, as they form the basis of the CHES® credential:

Area I: Assessment of Needs and Capacity
Area II: Planning
Area III: Implementation
Area IV: Evaluation and Research
Area V: Advocacy
Area VI: Communication
Area VII: Leadership and Management
Area VIII: Ethics and Professionalism[2]

From there it gets a bit more complicated, but we will walk you through it. A minimum of 12 semester hours/18 quarter hours must be from process courses that clearly align with the Eight Areas of Responsibility. Those courses might be called Program Planning, Program Evaluation, Research Methods, or Statistics, for example. As many as (but no more than) 9 semester hours/14 quarter hours may be from topic-focused courses that include elements contained in the Eight Areas of Responsibility, such as Health Communications and Worksite Health Promotion. Finally, as many as 6 semester hours/8 quarter hours may be from other

---

[2] The Eight Areas of Responsibility for Health Education Specialists are copyright of the National Commission for Health Education Credentialing, Inc. (NCHEC).

courses that include elements contained in the Eight Areas of Responsibility. Here you have a bit more flexibility, but the course has to be related to one of the Eight Areas—a budgeting class, for example.

So, look at your transcript. Identify the 25 hours you think apply to the Eight Areas. Then make sure at least 12 hours are method related, no more than 9 are topic focused, and no more than 6 are related to—but not wholly about—the Eight Areas of Responsibility. You can use this handy worksheet to organize your thoughts (Exhibit 1.1).

Exhibit 1.1 Worksheet for identifying qualifying credits for the CHES® exam

Must contain:
- 12 semester hours (18 quarter hours) from process courses that align with the Eight Areas of Responsibility
- 9 semester hours (14 quarter hours) (max) of topic-focused courses
- 6 semester hours (8 quarter hours) from other courses that include elements contained in the Seven Areas.

As a reminder, the Eight Areas of Responsibility for Health Education Specialists are:

Area I: Assessment of Needs and Capacity
Area II: Planning
Area III: Implementation
Area IV: Evaluation and Research
Area V: Advocacy
Area VI: Communication
Area VII: Leadership and Management
Area VIII: Ethics and Professionalism

Example:

| Course Name | Number of Credit Hours from Process Courses | Number of Credit Hours from Topic-Focused Courses | Number of Credit Hours from other Courses Related to the Eight Areas | |
|---|---|---|---|---|
| Program Planning and Evaluation | 3 | | | |
| Epidemiology | 3 | | | |
| Health Theories | 3 | | | |
| Public Health Research Methods | 3 | | | |
| Maternal and Child Health | | 3 | | |
| Social Marketing | | 3 | | |
| Healthcare Policy | | 3 | | |

(*continued*)

Exhibit 1.1 Worksheet for identifying qualifying credits for the CHES® exam

| Course Name | Number of Credit Hours from Process Courses | Number of Credit Hours from Topic-Focused Courses | Number of Credit Hours from other Courses Related to the Eight Areas | |
|---|---|---|---|---|
| Health Equity Research Methods | | | 3 | |
| Health Communications | | | 3 | |
| | | | | |
| Totals | 12 | 9 | 6 | |
| Grand Total: | | | | 27 hours |

Now here's a worksheet for your classes (Table 1.1):

**Table 1.1 Worksheet for identifying qualifying credits for the CHES® exam**

| Course Name | Number of Credit Hours from Process Courses | Number of Credit Hours from Topic-Focused Courses | Number of Credit Hours from Other Courses Related to the Eight Areas | |
|---|---|---|---|---|
| | | | | |
| | | | | |
| | | | | |
| | | | | |
| | | | | |
| | | | | |
| | | | | |
| | | | | |
| | | | | |
| | | | | |
| Totals | | | | |
| Grand Total: | | | | _____ hours |

If your degree is called "Health Behavior and Health Education," "Health Promotion and Behavior," "Behavioral and Community Health Sciences," or anything similar, you are probably OK. However, NCHEC does not refund your money if you apply for the exam and you do not actually qualify to take it. So it pays to be sure. You can check with your school to see if students with your degree or major have successfully taken the exam (talking to someone in Career Services might be a good place to start). But individuals can take different classes even within the same major, so you will want to confirm your particular course load with the stated requirements to make sure you qualify.

## ▶ PRESCREEN OR DON'T? UNDERSTANDING THE PRESCREENING OPTION

The best way to make sure that you are qualified to take the CHES® exam is to take advantage of NCHEC's Prescreen Service. Fill out the NCHEC's prescreen request form and submit it along with your official academic transcript(s) and a (nonrefundable) $25 fee. NCHEC will review your transcript(s) to determine if you are eligible. If you are missing certain classes, they will be identified and you will receive feedback on what you need to add to be eligible to sit the exam. If you do qualify to take the exam, NCHEC will credit the $25 you paid toward your exam fee. If you are unsure, it really pays to opt for the prescreen! It would be much better to lose $25 than the $100 nonrefundable application fee if it turns out you are not qualified! And the prescreening service has an additional benefit. The Prescreen Schedule is November 1 to January 31 for the April exam and May 1 to July 31 for the October exam, which may give current students time to register for any classes they are missing in time to take the exam for the next cycle. For example, you were hoping to take the exam in April with the 90-day option (more on that in a minute). You request a prescreen early in October and NCHEC tells you that you have only 9 of the required 12 semester hours of process classes. That should leave you time to sign up for a Program Planning class (or something similar) in the spring semester. Problem solved, and the $25 you spent for prescreening can be applied to your exam. Bottom line: If you are unsure, prescreen!

## ▶ APPLYING TO TAKE THE EXAM

Once you are sure you are eligible to take the exam, it is time to apply! The application process is fairly simple and can be completed online at www.nchec.org. The application process is handled through an online portal where you will create a username and password. If you prefer not to apply online, you can download a PDF of the application, fill it out, and email, fax, or mail it back in. If you mail it in, NCHEC recommends that you use Certified Mail, Federal Express, or some method of delivery that is trackable.

## ▶ EXAM DATES

The CHES® exam is offered twice every year, in April and October. If you are graduating in the semester in which you wish to take the exam, you may apply for the 90-Day Eligibility Option. To qualify for this option, a student must be enrolled in an accredited institution of higher education and must submit an official transcript showing a minimum of 25 semester hours relating to the Eight Areas of Responsibility along with written verification from a faculty advisor assuring the student will complete all the degree requirements within 90 days of the exam date. The advantages of taking the exam during your last semester are that you are still in "school mode"—the information from your classes is fresh in your mind and you are used to taking exams, to say nothing of being able to start your job search with a brand-new credential. And, of course, it would be wonderful to not have to take any more tests after you graduate! But there are some downsides to taking the test your last semester: you may already be overwhelmed with finishing a thesis, studying for finals, and applying for jobs. You certainly do not want to jeopardize your final semester's grades (and possibly graduation) with another exam to study for. So, if preparing for the CHES® exam is going to place too heavy a burden on you, remember that it will be offered again in 6 months. If you do choose the 90-Day Eligibility Option, NCHEC will withhold your credential until it receives your final transcripts.

## ▶ EXAM FEES

As in so many other situations, if you procrastinate in applying for the CHES® exam, it is going to cost you. The current fee schedule is in the following tables.

**Of course, these deadlines and fees can change, so be sure to check with NCHEC before you make any plans.**

Once your application is received and approved, you will receive instructions in the mail for scheduling your test. According to the NCHEC website, it is important to schedule your test as soon as possible, so do so as soon as your materials arrive (Tables 1.2 and 1.3).

**Table 1.2 October CHES® exam registration schedule and fees**

| October CHES® Exam | Nonstudent Fee | ᵃStudent Fee |
|---|---|---|
| Early Bird Registration: May 1–31 | $270 | $220 |
| Regular Registration: June 1–July 31 | $320 | $270 |
| Final (Late) Registration Deadline: August 31 | $370 | $320 |

ᵃ To qualify for the Student Fee rate, you must be enrolled in 9 or more credit hours (12 or more quarter hours) the semester you apply for the exam and/or provide documentation from your college/university of your full-time status.

**Table 1.3 April CHES® exam registration schedule and fees**

| April CHES® Exam | Nonstudent Fee | ᵃStudent Fee |
|---|---|---|
| Early Bird Registration: November 1–November 30 | $270 | $220 |
| Regular Registration: December 1–January 31 | $320 | $270 |
| Final (Late) Registration Deadline: February 28 | $370 | $320 |

A word on address changes: NCHEC will send test results to the address it has on file. So if you move, make sure to log on to the NCHEC website and update your contact information or call the office as soon as you know your new address.

## ▶ DAY OF TESTING—SCHEDULE AND ADVICE

The CHES® exam is offered at Prometric Testing Centers during a range of dates available each April and October.

You will schedule your test through the NCHEC website, which will take you directly to the Prometric website to locate a testing center near you. There are hundreds of testing sites in the United States and many internationally.

It is important to note that test takers may need accommodations during the test for many reasons (e.g., additional time to take the exam, breast-feeding, requiring a sign-language interpreter, needing a physical accommodation of some kind). Prometric lists many accommodations they are able to make for test takers on their website—it might be worth a look to see if any of the accommodations offered suit your particular needs. **Such accommodations must be approved by NCHEC BEFORE scheduling the exam (apart from additional time only).**

The day of testing will go much more smoothly if you have some idea what to expect. According to the Prometric website in September 2021, this is the check-in procedure:

- Original, valid (unexpired), government-issued photo and signature-bearing identification and your confirmation number are required to take an exam. NCHEC will determine which IDs are acceptable and communicate that to you prior to the test.
- You will be given a locker and a locker key. All coats, cell phones, hats, food, drinks, and so on must be stored in the locker. Any jewelry items other than wedding and/or engagement rings, as well as hair accessories (including headbands and barrettes) must be stored in your locker due to concerns over concealed recording devices.
- You may be scanned with a metal detector **prior to every entry** into the test room.
- You will be required to raise your pants legs above your ankles, empty and turn all pockets inside-out, and raise shirt sleeves above your wrists **prior to every entry** into the test room.
- If you are wearing eyeglasses, you will be required to remove them for visual inspection to ensure they do not contain a recording device.
- Additional COVID-19 safety protocols may be in place.

Prometric offers the *Test Drive* program, which, for a fee, allows those scheduled for a test to go to the center on a day before the exam and complete a "dry run" of the check-in, security, and testing procedures. According to its website, familiarity with the location and procedures of the exam will allow you to be better prepared on the actual exam day. For more information on Prometric and testing procedures, please visit www.prometric.com. Please check the NCHEC website for updates or changes to these procedures—it will always have the most up-to-date information.

## ⬤ TEST DAY: QUESTIONS AND ANSWERS

**Q** What can I bring to the exam?

**A** Not much. PURSES, FOOD, DRINKS, COATS, CELL PHONES, AND SO ON, WILL NOT BE ALLOWED AT YOUR SEAT. There will be lockers available to store those things, but it is best to leave as much in your car or at home as possible. All you may have at your seat are site-issued tissues and soft earplugs (without cords), or items that appear on the approved medical item list.

**Q** How can I keep track of time?

**A** The computer screen will keep time for you.

**Q** How long is the exam?

**A** Three hours.

**Q** What if I have to go to the bathroom?

**A** Each time you leave the test room, you must sign out. The testing center attendant will inform you of what is permitted during exam breaks, specifically whether access to your locker, and to the cell phone and notes within it, is allowed. All candidates must inform the testing center attendant before accessing a stored item—including medicine—during a break. Upon return from a break, without exception, you must go through all security checks, present valid ID, sign in, and, if required by the test sponsor, provide a fingerprint to be readmitted to the test room. Remember, the clock does not stop while you are out of the hall, so go quickly! Repeated or lengthy departures from the test room will be reported to NCHEC.

*(continued)*

**Q** What if I do not understand a question?

**A** If there is a mechanical problem with the computer (screen freezes or goes dark, etc.), inform the testing center attendant. If you do not understand the wording of a question or are not sure of an answer, the testing center attendant or fellow test takers cannot help you. Remember, 15 of the 165 questions are pretest questions, and the question that is stumping you could be one of those on the pretest. Just answer as best as you can and move on.

**Q** Is there a penalty for guessing?

**A** No, so do not leave a question unanswered! There are generally four potential multiple-choice answers, so even a random guess has a 25% chance of being right. If you can eliminate one or two of the answers, your odds are even higher. So do not leave anything blank!

**Q** What if I finish the exam before the 3 hours are up?

**A** Follow the on-screen prompts or the directions of the testing center administrator, who will collect all the testing material (including scratch paper, if it is available). You are then free to leave—but you may not come back, so take time to check your work and make sure you are really done!

## AFTER THE TEST: QUESTIONS AND ANSWERS

**Q** What is the pass rate for the CHES® Exam?

**A** It varies. According to NCHEC, it uses a criterion-referenced passing point technique that is an industry standard. Because there are multiple versions of the exam offered each year, the pass rate is slightly different for each one. For the two exams in 2020, the pass rate was between 64.96% and 73.81%.

**Q** What if my address changes after I take the exam but before results are mailed?

**A** Inform NCHEC on its website or call the office. Make sure you forward your mail through the U.S. Postal Service.

## ▶ CONCLUSION

Now that we have walked you through the process of applying for, taking, and waiting for the results of the CHES® exam, let us move on to reviewing the material that may be covered on the exam. Chapter 2 will start with Area I: Assessment of Needs and Capacity.

## REFERENCES

O*Net Online. (2021). Summary report for: 2101091.00—Health Education Specialists. Retrieved from https://www.onetonline.org/link/summary/21-1091.00

U.S. Department of Labor, Bureau of Labor Statistics. (2021, June). *Occupational outlook handbook. Health education specialists and community health workers.* Retrieved from https://www.bls.gov/ooh/community-and-social-service/health-educators.htm

# Area of Responsibility I: Assessment of Needs and Capacity[1]

## ▶ INTRODUCTION

This chapter covers assessing needs, assets, and capacity for health education. Health education specialists need to develop skills in the identification and use of existing data sources as well as analysis and interpretation of findings from the data. First we'll focus on how to use existing data and skills to conduct a needs assessment and interpret data, including existing data, and then focuses on the potential barriers and facilitators to health education programs.

## ▶ PLANNING A NEEDS ASSESSMENT

Needs assessment is one of the first strategies health educators use to understand health behaviors and problems, as well as resources and barriers. According to the National Commission for Health Education Credentialing (NCHEC), the Society for Public Health Education (SOPHE), and the American Association for Health Education (AAHE), a key area of responsibility for entry- and advanced-level health educators is the assessment of individual and community needs for health education. A needs assessment includes obtaining health-related data, distinguishing between behaviors that enhance and impede well-being, and understanding the broader needs of the setting (e.g., schools, worksites, healthcare organizations, and community) for health education. A health educator should consider ways to collect this information and include aspects of the needs assessment in their program planning and evaluation.

### NEEDS ASSESSMENTS AND CAPACITY BUILDING ARE ESSENTIAL FOR PLANNING FOR HEALTH EDUCATION

A needs assessment gathers information to determine the most appropriate health education activities given the needs and setting. Needs assessments ask about the essential needs of an individual or a priority population and should encourage equity and social justice principles (Gilmore, 2012).

A **needs assessment** is a systematic, planned collection of information about the health knowledge, perceptions, attitudes, motivation, and practices of individuals or groups and the quality of their environment. It is also a process to address gaps between what is currently happening and setting future goals. Information gleaned from the needs assessment can also inform the evaluation of a health education program (Harris, 2010).

---

[1]The Eight Areas of Responsibility for Health Education Specialists are copyright of the National Commission for Health Education Credentialing, Inc. (NCHEC).

Goals of a needs assessment include: (a) identifying and prioritizing health problems, (b) prioritizing the strategies and methods that will be ideal for identifying and addressing these health problems through both existing and available resources, and (c) identifying additional resources that will support addressing the identified health problems (Gilmore, 2012).

## ▶ ASSESSING CAPACITY

**Capacity** is defined as both individual and collective resources that can be used for health enhancement (Gilmore, 2012). You can assess capacity by identifying areas that may need to be enhanced before implementing a health education program to sustain the program over the long term. Capacity assessment includes examining potential assets and strengths at the individual, group, and community levels. A capacity assessment measures actual or potential resources that can aid in the maintenance and enhancement of health education programs. For example, The Centers for Disease Control and Prevention (CDC) Diabetes Prevention Recognition Programs use capacity assessments to determine whether organizations have the capacity to deliver approved type 2 diabetes prevention lifestyle interventions (CDC, n.d.). In this case, the assessment includes identifying eligible participants from a community (individual level), assessing whether the organization's staff have the capacity needed (appropriate knowledge, skills, and qualities) to lead the health education program (group level), and whether there is the appropriate level of resources to maintain the program long term, including the availability of federal, state, or local grant funding (community level; CDC, 2013).

## ▶ KEY STEPS OF A NEEDS ASSESSMENT[2]

A needs assessment often includes examining both quantitative and qualitative data. These data can help health educators understand the expressed and observed needs for health education programs. Conducting a needs assessment requires the health educator to follow a process that engages multiple stakeholders and various data collection sources and methods. Such data will help validate the need and develop a roadmap to follow before planning the health education program.

1. Determine the purpose of the needs assessment and priority population(s).
2. Identify available data to assess the health problem.
3. Decide on the data collection approach and gather data.
4. Analyze and interpret the data.
5. Identify factors linked to the health problem(s).
6. Identify the focus of the program and begin the planning process.

### DETERMINE THE PURPOSE OF THE NEEDS ASSESSMENT AND PRIORITY POPULATION(S)

To effectively plan a needs assessment, it is essential to first understand how it will be used and who will participate in the needs assessment process. Critical components include having the most appropriate needs assessment strategy and having a general idea of human and financial

---

[2] Competency 1.1 Plan Assessment, copyright of the National Commission for Health Education Credentialing, Inc. (NCHEC).

resources available for the assessment. Defining the priority population, or "who" is being assessed, is an essential first step in conducting the needs assessment. A priority population might be the entire population of a community or subgroups. This often requires knowledge of the priority population's background, including age, gender, educational attainment, income, geographic location, culture, religious beliefs, and other demographic characteristics.

Health educators should ask the following questions when determining the purpose of the needs assessment and priority population:

- "What is the purpose of the needs assessment?"
- "What do we hope to gain from doing the needs assessment?"
- "What will be used to determine the priority population's knowledge, attitudes, beliefs, behaviors, skills, and/or health status?"
- "Who is the priority population(s)? "
- "Where is the population(s) located in the community?"
- "What historical or current issues impact the priority population(s)?"

What three factors should be identified in a needs assessment?

1. Predisposing Factors—represent cognitive, emotional, social, and demographic factors that may contribute to one's health behaviors or motivations for such behaviors. Predisposing factors may include knowledge, beliefs, attitudes, intentions, and demographic factors.
2. Enabling Factors—often represent the internal and external conditions directly related to the issue that help people adopt and maintain healthy or unhealthy behaviors and lifestyles, or to embrace or reject particular environmental conditions. Enabling factors can include skills, various types of resources (e.g., informational, financial, and social support), and environmental factors that may facilitate or impede behavior change.
3. Reinforcing Factors—represent those factors that help to remind, provide feedback, and provide ongoing support to ensure that health behaviors are maintained or terminated. Examples included daily reminders via text message, peer support groups, and daily affirmations. Identifying these factors can help health educators better understand what aspects may be influencing health behavior at the individual, group, and community levels. Often at the community level, people represent sources of influence, such as family members, peers, teachers, employers, health providers, the media, community leaders, politicians, and other decision-makers.

—Green & Kreuter (1992)

Health educators should establish a set of parameters for conducting the needs assessment. Identifying these parameters early on is necessary for completing the needs assessments, and health educators should consider utilizing a model to guide the needs assessment, such as the Epidemiological Model, Public Health Model, Social Model, Asset Model (AM), PRECEDE-PROCEED Model (Green & Kreuter, 1992; see Chapter 3), or the Rapid Model (Issel, 2004).

For example, the Epidemiological Model supports a needs assessments for a given priority population by objectively measuring those problems that pose the greatest threat to health and quality of life. One fundamental way the Epidemiological Model does this is by examining the distribution and determinants of health problems or events in terms of the population. Key questions include:

- What is the problem?
- Who has the problem?
- Why do those with the problem have it?

The Public Health Model is another model for conducting needs assessments similar to the Epidemiological Model. The Public Health Model focuses on quantifying health problems through existing and epidemiological data. However, it tends to focus on a specific priority population and is a valuable model when you have limited resources.

There are also models more appropriate for conducting a community needs assessment. For example, two commonly used models include the Planned Approach to Community Health (PATCH) and Mobilizing for Action through Planning and Partnership (MAPP). Both of these community health planning models focus on identifying assets and needs by utilizing community engagement, followed by developing the plan, conducting the health education program or intervention, and then evaluating the program (CDC, 2014).

The Social Model for needs assessment focuses on identifying pertinent social, economic, and political issues that influence health (Issel, 2004). The model emphasizes the role of societal trends in the needs assessment and relies on collecting data on social indicators, such as income, social norms, and other social resources. Potential sources of social indicator data come from the U.S. Census Surveys (Census, 2015), including the American Community Survey (ACS), the American Housing Survey (AHS), the Current Population Survey (CPS), the Consumer Expenditure Survey (CES), and the National Health Interview Survey (NHIS).

Another model for conducting needs assessments that focuses more on strengths is the Asset Model (AM). This model involves an assessment of the strengths of a community, group, organization, or priority population by examining existing assets that can help improve health. An assets-based assessment focuses specifically on

- identifying available community resources,
- creating or strengthening relationships between community members and organizations,
- mobilizing the community around its strengths and resources,
- rallying the community to develop a shared health vision for the future, and
- introducing outside resources to fill identified gaps.

Thus, an AM focuses on a community or group's potential social capital (both community and social resources) given a particular health problem. AMs also focus on **community competence**—a community's ability to identify health problems and take action to address these health problems. Some commonly used AMs for addressing a community's strengths include Kretzmann and McKnight's (1996) Asset-Based Community Development (ABCD) and the AM, which involves increasing the participation of local communities to assess current health problems (Morgan & Ziglio, 2007).

The Rapid Model is another tool for conducting needs assessments when there is limited time, an in-depth assessment is not practical, or there is an impending crisis (i.e., a pandemic or catastrophic flood) that requires immediate action. A health educator would use a rapid needs assessment to collect information quickly, especially when time and money are limited. Example methods include:

- brief key informant interviews
- focus groups
- use of existing data (e.g., local data from hospitals, health departments, and other emergency response organizations)
- data from the impacted community to rapidly develop and implement health interventions

Two commonly used rapid assessment models include Rapid Assessment and Response (RAR) and Rapid Assessment and Response and Evaluation (RARE). Both models assess complex health issues and behaviors within a short time frame and facilitate rapid response with appropriate health education program measures and interventions (Issel, 2004; Trotter et al., 2001).

## IDENTIFY AVAILABLE DATA TO ASSESS THE HEALTH PROBLEM[3]

It is essential to locate existing data as well as plan for collecting new data. There may also be useful secondary data (existing data on the impact of programs and services, resources, research outcomes, and public policies). Using secondary data can help to save time, money, and other resources. It is important to conduct a thorough review of the available data from your local communities as well as any state, regional, and national data sources. Often local public health agencies, healthcare organizations, or community organizations are already conducting or planning to collect data that a health educator can utilize for their needs assessment. While existing data may be helpful in understanding the health problems of a specific group, health educators will likely need to collect additional data.

Sources of data:

1. **Primary data** involves the collection of original or new data. Primary data often take the most time to collect and requires greater financial and data collection resources. Thus, health educators often rely on previously collected data from secondary and/or tertiary data.
2. **Secondary data** involves data collected by others, and it is often readily available and inexpensive to obtain. Potential secondary data sources may include: federal, state, and local health departments; federally qualified health centers; hospitals; and other health organizations. Secondary data may include mortality and morbidity rates from disease, injury, and disability. Sources of secondary data may include: Morbidity and Mortality Weekly Report (*MMWR*) from the CDC; the annual Behavioral Risk Factor Surveillance System (CDC), the NHIS (CDC), hospital data such as vital statistics and electronic health records; and data from peer-reviewed health education, medical, and interdisciplinary journals.
3. **Tertiary data** may include other publications, such as encyclopedias, pamphlets, fact sheets, websites, and other reference tools that summarize the findings of primary and secondary data sources.

## DECIDE ON THE DATA COLLECTION APPROACH AND GATHER DATA

After reviewing existing data, health educators play an important role in determining additional data collection approaches that will be needed to gather other valuable data. Select the best data collection methods that will be useful and fit within the predetermined timeline. Health educators should collect data by using the most appropriate research methods. There are several key issues to consider when collecting data for a needs assessment:

- data needed
- data collection methods
- sampling techniques
- research design
- validity and reliability of instruments

---

[3] Competency 1.2 Obtain primary data, secondary data, and other evidence-informed sources, copyright of the National Commission for Health Education Credentialing, Inc. (NCHEC).

The data needed for the needs assessment should tie back to the purpose of the needs assessment, including the priority population and available resources for the needs assessment. Due to the limited resources for data collection, health educators often must restrict data collection to the minimum amount of data necessary to address the needs of the priority population.

Which data collection method a health educator chooses for a needs assessment can affect how the information can be used. It may be important to collect data from a range of sources, including:

- secondary and tertiary data:
  - archival data (medical or agency records)
  - publicly available data (CDC or other national data)
  - published literature (literature reviews or summaries of other published works)

- primary data sources:
  - surveys
  - interviews
  - observations
  - community forums
  - focus group
  - nominal group process
  - delphi panel
  - self-assessment instruments
  - community capacity data
  - observational data (environmental scan of health behaviors, such as public smoking or tobacco-related advertisements in convenience stores)
  - other sources (community stakeholder input, local news, and social media)

## Literature Reviews

A literature review is a document that summarizes key sources on a health education topic. It synthesizes (i.e., compares, contrasts, analyzes, interprets) these sources across a specific topic or identified areas. Often literature reviews are organized in chronologic, thematic, methodologic, or theoretical aspects of the broader literature. Sometimes literature reviews are limited to only peer-reviewed literature or gray literature. Gray literature comprises sources from nontraditional publishing, such as reports, policies, white papers, news, government documents, websites, and other sources.

## PRIMARY DATA COLLECTION METHODS—QUALITATIVE

Qualitative research is a broad methodologic approach that seeks to understand a situation by exploring the perspectives of those involved in the situation. Qualitative researchers use various qualitative methods to gain understanding. This section will review four commonly used qualitative methods in health education.

### What Is a Focus Group?

A focus group is a qualitative method where, generally speaking, a group of 6 to 10 individuals are invited to participate in a group interview about their perceptions, opinions, beliefs, and/ or attitudes toward a specific health concern or issue. The discussion is led by a moderator, who poses questions and probes from a predeveloped guide. The moderator must ensure the discussion covers the desired topics, obtains insight into the topic within the allotted time frame, and that all participants are encouraged to share their perspectives. Focus groups are often designed to be homogeneous around a characteristic of interest if a topic is sensitive (e.g. race/ethnicity, gender, religion, age, politics, or difficult topics such as interpersonal violence) so that participants feel comfortable sharing information and common frames of reference and experiences.

## What Is a Key Informant Interview?

An interviewer also hosts key informant interviews, but generally, the participants are interviewed one or two at time. Often, key informants will be experts on the health topic or issue and can identify other key informants who should be interviewed. Key informant interviews allow for more in-depth probing of the participant's perspective than what is possible during a focus group and are appropriate to gain knowledge from people with particular expertise or insight into a topic. Key informant interviews may also be more suitable for very sensitive topics where people might not be willing to share information in a group setting; the interviewer can develop a better rapport with the participant than may be possible in group settings. The downside of the method is that it is very time-consuming to collect and analyze multiple key informant interviews and related data.

## What Is a Nominal Group Process?

In nominal group process, a small group of individuals respond to questions, discuss answers, and then privately rank the importance of these health concerns or issues. The individual rankings are then shared with the group and tallied by the moderator. This process is repeated as necessary to achieve group consensus. Advantages of nominal group process are that it is a democratic way of making decisions, often can better reflect community/group priorities, and works well to ensure that everyone has a say in the decisions being made, which can neutralize any pressure from others who have competing priorities or may be less inclusive of others' views and opinions. Disadvantages of the method are that it requires some preparation, takes time, and is relatively regimented, which can lead to less-than-developed ideas being enacted.

## What Is a Delphi Panel Process?

A Delphi panel process is used when there is no clear evidence base from which to make decisions, so this process takes advantage of the wisdom of experts to make decisions or recommendations. Delphi panels distribute structured questionnaires to experts or thought leaders about a particular topic. The questionnaires are revised each time (range of 3–5 times) and sent back to participants to achieve consensus across the panel.

**Triangulation** means exploring multiple points of view, angles, and perspectives in a given setting, establishing "dialogue" among these perspectives, and integrating them into the analysis of findings. In a broader research context, triangulation may also involve employing multiple and differing methodological approaches and qualitative and quantitative data, different sources of information, and differing theoretical perspectives to study a given question or setting. Despite the name, these approaches, instruments, sources, perspectives, and so on, do not need to be limited to only three sources.

## PRIMARY DATA COLLECTION METHODS—QUANTITATIVE

### Survey Research Method

Surveys are one of the most popular tools for primary data collection. They are relatively inexpensive to develop, distribute, and analyze. Depending on your population and topic of interest, substantial data can be obtained from surveys to inform your health education efforts and programmatic choices (Aday & Cornelius, 2011). No wonder they are so frequently used by health educators to assess needs, plan, and evaluate programs! However, there are some limitations to keep in mind: surveys can have meager response rates, especially without incentives. Depending on the population of interest, surveys can be challenging to get into the hands of the people you are most interested in hearing from (especially for vulnerable populations, e.g., the homeless, those who cannot read, displaced populations, the very young and very old). Still, they remain a critical tool for a health educator.

Many health educators also have access to online tools for survey development. These survey platforms (e.g., SurveyMonkey and Qualtrics) are helpful because survey creators can share them via email, text message, quick response (QR) codes, and flyers. These platforms also offer some tools to support summarizing and analyzing data. However, it is important to consider the cost and ensure that appropriate measures are in place to protect participants' personal information.

There are four steps that you should consider when developing a survey.

1. Plan the survey by determining objectives and resources.
2. Design the survey to meet the objectives within the scope of the available resources.
3. Collect data that ensures the objectives will be achieved and the survey is in line with the available resources.
4. Plan for the data analysis and ensure that the goals and objectives of the needs assessment are met.

Choosing an appropriate research design is important for health educators who are collecting primary data. Typically, health educators will use observational methods to better understand how various factors may result in a health problem or condition. Observational designs include **cross-sectional** (one-time point for data collection—present or recall of past); group comparisons, including **case-control** (which matches an intervention participant with a control participant [present and recall of past]); and **longitudinal** (prospective and includes present and future data) designs (Aday & Cornelius, 2011).

Experimental designs include both present and past data, but participants are randomly assigned to either the experimental or control group. Experimental designs are usually not appropriate for needs assessments but should be considered if the data could be used during the program evaluation stage. Barriers to using experimental designs include being very expensive and relying on a control group (individual or community) to compare the effects of a health education intervention. Also, the control group needs to be equivalent to the experimental group.

For nonexperimental designs, various sampling techniques can be used, such as convenience or **snowball sampling**, which represents recruitment by word-of-mouth or referrals from other participants. The sample will depend on the accessibility of the priority population and the sample size needed.

When constructing a survey or choosing existing data collection tools, it is also important to consider both the validity and reliability of the tools.

**Validity** refers to the degree the instrument measures what it is intended to measure.

**Reliability** is concerned with the degree to which the instrument yields the same results each time it is used and when it is used with different populations.

When constructing a new survey, pretest the survey with a group or population similar to the priority populations for the needs assessment. Based on the pretest, you may need to revise and retest the survey until you are sure it will capture the needed data.

## ANALYZE AND INTERPRET THE DATA[4]

Health educators need to rely on data analysts and others who can aid in turning raw data into useful information for program planning and evaluation. They also need to answer the questions being asked as part of a health education program and its outcomes. Remember that even copious, high-quality data will mean nothing if they are not correctly analyzed or not analyzed at all.

Data analysis does not necessarily mean using complicated data analysis software. It may just involve looking at the data you collected and determining whether the data can help you answer the questions you need to answer. For example, if you need to know whether your health education program is meeting its objectives or if it is on track, you can look at your program targets and compare them to the actual program performance.

There are seven steps in analyzing survey data:

1. Administer survey—method should fit with program objectives
2. Prepare data—code question/answers; limit and check for any data entry errors
3. Verify data—test for accuracy or coding errors
4. Enter data—this can be a spreadsheet or a specific data software
5. Tabulate data—this involves organizing the data in terms of a table or spreadsheet containing rows and columns
6. Analyze data—possibly with descriptive statistics or analyzes related to key questions or hypotheses
7. Record and report data—should include objectives, hypothesis, survey steps description, reliability of results, and details on the sample's background characteristics

### Descriptive Analysis Terms

Descriptive analysis—describes the sample or priority populations. It does not define causality.

Example: Average number of clients seen per month.

Additional examples of descriptive analysis:

Rates—one measure in respect to another measure in terms of quantity over the same time period. Example—The health education intervention increased knowledge by 80%.

Mean—average score or represents the values obtained by dividing the sum of a set of quantities by the number of quantities in the set. Example—The average age of participants was 25 years old.

Median—the middle of a distribution of a set of values. Example—For the following list of numbers (2, 3, 3, 4, 5, 5, 6), the median or middle number is 4.

Like analyzing data, health educators need to know how to use needs assessment data. Below is a list of the steps in analyzing assessment findings (McKenzie et al., 2016):

---

[4] Competency 1.3 Analyze the data to determine the health of the priority population(s) and the factors that influence health, copyright of the National Commission for Health Education Credentialing, Inc. (NCHEC).

1. Analyze data.
2. Compare with local, state, or national data.
3. Consider the social, cultural, and political environment.
4. Set priorities.

    a. Assess the size and scope of the problem.

    b. Determine the effectiveness of possible interventions.

    c. Determine appropriateness, economics, acceptability, resources, and legality of interventions.

For intervention mapping, there are five steps to consider (Bartholomew et al., 1998):

1. Create a matrix of the immediate program objectives.
2. Select a theory- or evidence-based intervention with appropriate methods and strategies.
3. Design and organize the intervention.
4. Specify the implementation plans.
5. Generate the program evaluation plans.

## Primary, Secondary, and Tertiary Prevention (Gordon, 1983; World Health Organization, 2017)

**Primary prevention** involves delaying or preventing illness or injury.

| |
|---|
| Examples:<br>Implementing a routine immunization program for children.<br>Eliminating environmental risks for diseases, such as contaminated water.<br>Enhancing the nutritional status of low-income mothers. |

**Secondary prevention** involves an effort to diagnose an illness or injury early and/or encourage early treatment.

| |
|---|
| Examples:<br>Routine screening for major forms of cancer<br>Early detection of risk for falls among older adults<br>Conducting health screening for inner-city youth at risk for type 2 diabetes. |

**Tertiary prevention** focuses on providing treatment and recovery from an illness or injury.

| |
|---|
| Examples:<br>Increasing access to affordable treatments for individuals with early-stage cancers.<br>Providing medicines, such as inhalers and bronchodilators, to steelworkers at risk for asthma.<br>Offering free outpatient treatment for individuals with hypertension. |

# IDENTIFY FACTORS LINKED TO THE HEALTH PROBLEM[5]

In the needs assessment phase, you should consider different factors influencing health. There are several ways to do this, including assessing the social determinates of health and the social-ecological model. According to Healthy People 2030, the social determinants of health "are conditions in the environments where people are born, live, learn, work, play, worship, and age that affect a wide range of health, functioning, and quality-of-life outcomes and risks" and include economic stability, neighborhood and built environment, health and healthcare, social and community context, and education (Office of Disease Prevention and Health Promotion, n.d.). The social-ecological model is a systems model that surrounds the individual with multiple bands of influence, radiating out from the individual through the interpersonal, to institutions, the community, and finally to public policy and laws. At the needs assessment level, health educators should consider which factors—biological, behavioral, environmental, policy, and so on—are involved in creating the health problem of interest.

Now that you have the data you need, it is time to synthesize the findings to inform the health education program planning, implementation, and future evaluation. First, you should compare the results to other existing data and knowledge on the priority population and health topics of interest. You may need to compare findings to secondary data and published research or obtain community views on whether the findings reflect current knowledge, beliefs, and norms.

It may be important to summarize findings, develop a written report, and provide recommendations to key stakeholders and community members to ensure that the recommendations and plans align with the needs of the priority population. When developing your report, include the following: (a) an overview of the health issue or problem, (b) a data and analysis plan, (c) results of your data analysis, and (d) conclusions and recommendations.

## ▶ BARRIERS AND FACILITATORS TO HEALTH EDUCATION

Health promotion and education often focuses on behaviors or risk factor rather than identifying the range of social and environmental factors that affect health behaviors (Robinson et al., 2006). For more information on facilitating adult learning, see Chapter 3. For information on writing learning objectives, including Bloom's Taxonomy, see Chapter 3.

Interpersonal health behaviors are typically the product of the interaction between individual and environmental factors. To drive behavior change, individuals need to develop supportive beliefs, training, and/or skills; they may need incentives; and the social and physical environment needs to support the behavior change.

As mentioned earlier, facilitators and barriers to health education programs may include attitudes (predisposing factors); the necessary action, skills, and resources that enable behavior change and feedback (reinforcing factors); and social aspects such as friends, family, coworkers, and classmates (enabling factors) (Green & Kreuter, 1992).

From socioecological theory, the interconnections between groups and organizations and the broader environmental context may also influence health promotion and education efforts positively or negatively (Robinson et al., 2006). In health education, it is important to acknowledge and identify social, cultural, political, economic, and environmental factors that influence the health of communities (Glanz et al., 2008). Thus, it is important that health education identify and develop plans to address potential facilitators and barriers to health education.

---

[5] Competency 1.4 Synthesize assessment finding to inform the planning process, copyright of the National Commission for Health Education Credentialing, Inc. (NCHEC).

## POTENTIAL BARRIERS TO HEALTH EDUCATION

Inadequate health literacy (poor communication; Bensley & Brookins-Fisher, 2009)
- Competing priorities or lack of interest
- Lack of skilled and/or committee people
- Lack of funds and resources
- Lack of leadership
- Unsupportive environment
- Transportation or geographic challenges
- Lack of time
- Weak partnerships

## POTENTIAL FACILITATORS OF HEALTH EDUCATION

Strong partnerships
- Sustaining structure/coordination
- Evidence that the health education/promotion program works
- Adapts to needs
- Good communication
- Funds and resources
- Low response burden

## IDENTIFY THE FOCUS OF THE PROGRAM AND BEGIN THE PLANNING PROCESS

Once you have conducted and analyzed your needs assessment, your work is not quite finished. Your last step should be to return to your priority populations and validate what you think you have found with them to make sure you have heard what they have said. Just as you likely used multiple methods to uncover needs in the population, you will likely use multiple methods to "check back" with them to synthesize and prioritize needs. You will have to decide which needs are more and less changeable and which are of greater and lesser importance. This will help you as you move into the next phase—program planning. Often, needs assessment ends with some kind of reporting process, which can be formal or informal. Consider reporting in a variety of formats, as appropriate to your audience, including written reports, in-person presentations, online and/or social media posts, and infographics. Remember to make reports accessible in terms of reading levels, languages, and disabilities. Next, it is time to start the planning process and prioritize health education and promotion needs.

## ▶ CONCLUSION

A needs assessment is a critical first step in developing health education programs and materials that will have the maximum positive effect and avoid wasting time or resources, or creating unintended consequences. Think of it as the foundation on which you build your health education house—a weak foundation will lead to building problems down the line. In the next chapter, we will review how to apply the results of the needs assessment to the next step in the process—planning for health education/promotion, which is Area of Responsibility II.

1. Which of the following is true about participant observation?

   A. It can provide guidance on sampling interviewees
   B. It must include formal interviews in the field
   C. It yields the best results when it is covert
   D. It usually is just done for short periods of time

2. Which statement is true about interviewers during qualitative, in-depth interviews?

   A. They try to avoid using probes or follow-up questions
   B. They read each question exactly as it appears on the interview questionnaire
   C. They need to convey genuine interest in the interviewee's responses
   D. They agree with the participant's responses and take their side to build rapport

3. A health educator is conducting a community needs assessment on pediatric dental care. In the focus groups, several parents mention that they struggle with finding convenient and affordable transportation to get their child to the dentist. This is an example of a:

   A. Predisposing factor
   B. Enabling factor
   C. Reinforcing factor
   D. Lifestyle factor

4. Which statement is true about selection in qualitative research?

   A. A researcher does not need to write a strategy for selecting cases in the research proposal. The best strategy will become apparent as the research proceeds
   B. Participants can help recruit other participants
   C. In selecting participants, a researcher should strive for maximum variation
   D. If possible, random sampling is the gold standard

5. Which one is NOT true about someone who uses qualitative research methods?

   A. They often assume an identity other than their own
   B. They use rigorous, systematic methods
   C. They usually need to interact with people in the setting to gain access
   D. They can change the data collection strategy if the initial data suggest this is necessary

6. Which of these ethical considerations does NOT apply to participant observation?

   A. Not harming the participants
   B. Ensuring the participants' privacy
   C. Ensuring that all participants provide written informed consent
   D. Being respectful of cultural differences

*(See answers next page.)*

## 1. C) It yields the best results when it is covert

Participant observation includes developing rapport, taking extensive, reflexive field notes (usually not during the observations, but afterward), and in many cases, interviews. Because it is an immersive technique, you would not set up a purposive sampling technique.

## 2. C) They need to convey genuine interest in the interviewee's responses

While remaining pleasant, a good interviewer builds rapport, asks questions, uses probes, and conveys interest in the interviewee while remaining neutral during an interview.

## 3. B) Enabling factor

Enabling factors are those resources, individual or structural, that enable or increase the likelihood of a behavior occurring.

## 4. B) Participants can help recruit other participants

Unlike in quantitative data collection, you can often use participants in qualitative data collection to help identify and recruit appropriate participants for qualitative data through snowball sampling.

## 5. A) They often assume an identity other than their own

In general, when using qualitative methods, we do not change our identity. In fact, the principles of informed consent nearly always dictate that we fully disclose who we are as researchers and what we are doing in a particular study.

## 6. C) Ensuring that all participants provide written informed consent

By nature, it is impossible to provide written (or even verbal) informed consent when conducting a participant observation study because the researcher is unobtrusively observing the behavior of the participants.

7. Coding is a qualitative analytic technique used to:

   A. Eliminate unimportant data
   B. Sort and categorize themes and concepts by labeling them
   C. Create comprehensive lists of corresponding symbols
   D. Coordinate triangulation among different theories

8. If a respondent does NOT understand the question during a telephone survey, the interviewer should:

   A. Rephrase the question in local terms, based on familiarity with the area
   B. Read the question or clarifying text in the survey again
   C. Go to the next question
   D. Try to guess the best answer, given the respondent's characteristics

9. Close-ended questions:

   A. Are not popular in survey research
   B. Are easier to recode and analyze
   C. Encourage the respondent to elaborate on responses
   D. Should have a few, general response categories

10. What is the major weakness of this survey item?

   *"How old were you when your parents first took you to a restaurant?"*

   1. *Under 6 months old*
   2. *6–12 months old*
   3. *13–24 months old*
   4. *25 months to 3 years old*
   5. *Older than 3 years old*
   6. *They never took me to a restaurant*

   A. It is double-barreled
   B. It is not mutually exclusive
   C. Respondents are not fully capable of answering
   D. It uses jargon

## 7. B) Sort and categorize themes and concepts by labeling them

Qualitative data is coded, or sorted, and categorized into themes and concepts by labeling them in ways that make sense to the researchers who are trying to answer questions about the participants.

## 8. B) Read the question or clarifying text in the survey again

When administering a telephone survey, it is important to stick to the written script of materials. Rereading questions and clarifying text is fine, but rephrasing material or guessing a participant's responses is not.

## 9. B) Are easier to recode and analyze

One of the advantages of using close-ended questions in survey research is that they are easy to analyze, which is one of the reasons why they are so popular. A disadvantage is that they do not elicit further information from respondents.

## 10. C) Respondents are not fully capable of answering

Respondents would not be able to remember when they were that young, and so would not be able to answer the question appropriately.

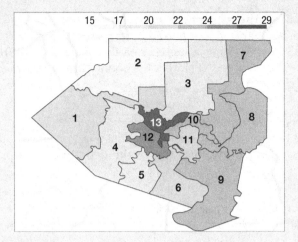

**Figure 2.1** County prevalence of depression by district

Use Figure 2.1 for questions 11 and 12.

11. A health educator is presented with data of the lifetime prevalence of depression by district with this county. Which of the following can be said?

   A. The prevalence of depression ranges from 1% to 13%
   B. Districts 12 and 13 have the highest rates of depression
   C. District 11 has higher rates of depression than District 5
   D. Living on the east side of the county reduces the likelihood of experiencing depression

12. After reviewing the data in Figure 2.1, the health educator is concerned about rates of depression in several districts within the county. Which of the following would be a primary source of data for a needs assessment?

   A. Published data from the county health department
   B. Review of hospital admissions for suicide attempts
   C. Interviews with crisis response workers
   D. Review of claims paid by insurance companies for depression-related treatments

13. What is NOT true of a good health-related research question?

   A. Can be answered empirically
   B. Identifies a topic but never a specific population
   C. Can be written as a question
   D. Is ethical

14. "Colorectal cancer among African American men in Alabama":

   A. Is not a good research question because the population is too specific
   B. Is a topic, not a question
   C. Can become a good research question as: "How can we eliminate the problem of colorectal cancer for African American men in Alabama?"
   D. Can become a good research question as: "What are the evidence-based interventions to detect colorectal cancer among African American men?"

## 11. B) Districts 12 and 13 have the highest rates of depression

Figure 2.1 shows that Districts 12 and 13 have the highest rates of depression. Prevalence ranges from 15% to 29% and District 5 has a higher rate than District 11. While rates vary across the county, generally rates on the east side of the county are higher than rates on the west side.

## 12. C) Interviews with crisis response workers

Interviews conducted by the health educator would be considered primary data collection— the others are reviewing data collected by others (the health department, hospitals, or health insurance companies).

## 13. B) Identifies a topic but never a specific population

Health-related research questions are nearly always related to specific populations.

## 14. B) Is a topic, not a question

Colorectal cancer among African American men in Alabama is a topic, not a question. Neither of the research questions listed is workable—the first because it is highly unlikely that colorectal cancer could ever be eliminated because it has multiple determinates, all of which would need to be addressed differently. The second, "What are the evidence-based interventions to detect colorectal cancer" is not a research question—that information exists and is discoverable through a literature search.

15. Low reach, a skewed older population, a low response rate, and the inability to interpret body language are all limitations of what kinds of survey technique?

   A. Focus group
   B. Telephone
   C. Face-to-face
   D. Web-based

16. The best data for understanding the needs of your audience generally comes from:

   A. A large investment in primary research
   B. A combination of secondary sources and qualitative and quantitative primary research
   C. Extensive use of focus groups and in-depth interviews to gain rich, deep data about the audience and their needs
   D. An exhaustive review of the literature

17. "The population in County A experiences larger morbidity rates for several diseases than County B. Both counties have similar per capita income. Therefore, the health differences must be caused by something other than income level." This is an example of:

   A. Tautology
   B. Reductionism
   C. Ecological fallacy
   D. Spuriousness

18. What conclusions can you draw from the chart in Figure 2.2?

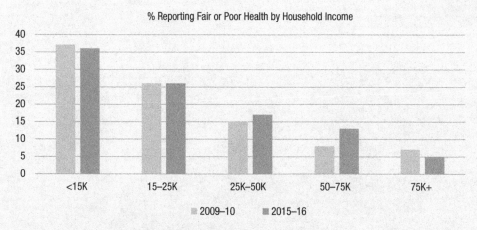

% Reporting Fair or Poor Health by Household Income

■ 2009–10    ■ 2015–16

**Figure 2.2** Percentage reporting fair or poor health by household income

   A. Health disparities based on income are declining
   B. The prevalence of fair/poor health is increasing
   C. The odds of reporting fair/poor health are about 6 to 7 times higher in people earning <$15K compared to people earning $75K+
   D. The odds of reporting fair/poor health are about 3 times lower in people earning $15 to $25k compared to people earning <$15K

## 15. B) Telephone

Telephone surveys often rely on landlines, which are increasingly rare and more common in households with older people. There is a relatively low response rate with such surveys and they can miss important body language and other visual information.

## 16. B) A combination of secondary sources and qualitative and quantitative primary research

The combination of secondary sources—which can tell you what has been tried in the past, what has been successful, and what has not— that can provide you with vital statistics, demographics, and so on, and a mixed-methods primary research strategy that can provide specific generalizable data as well as rich, deep qualitative data, is most likely to yield a health educator with the best information from which to plan a program.

## 17. C) Ecological fallacy

Ecological fallacy is an error made in reasoning about different units of analysis. Specifically, it is an error of using data generated from groups as the unit of analysis and attempting to draw conclusions about individuals. Per capita income is a summary measure at the level of the county (which is the unit of analysis). We do not have any information about the distribution of income among individuals. Therefore, we do not know if income is related to health outcomes or not, which is a different unit of analysis (the individual level).

## 18. C) The odds of reporting fair/poor health are about 6 to 7 times higher in people earning <$15K compared to people earning $75K+

19. Figure 2.3 shows provisional mortality from COVID-19 in the state of Texas in December 2020 and a year later in December 2021. Based on the data shown, which is NOT true?

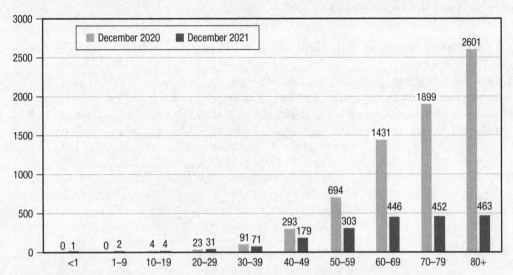

**Figure 2.3** (Selected) Provisional Texas COVID-19 fatality demographics, by age group, by month

A. Mortality was higher in every age category in 2020
B. The biggest improvements in mortality were in the 80+ demographic
C. Data variability increased in 2021
D. COVID-19 deaths remained steady or decreased from the December 2020 to December 2021 periods for people under 40

20. A health educator is planning to conduct a needs assessment with immigrant and refugee populations to understand their barriers to using primary care services at a local health center. After examining secondary data, they intend to collect primary data from the population. As part of their primary data collection they should plan to do all of the following except:

A. Identify priority populations within the immigrant and refugee community
B. Secure funding for incentives and other data collection needs
C. Compare these current client satisfaction metrics to those from the previous year
D. Create or adapt data collection instruments

**19. A) Mortality was higher in every age category in 2020**
Mortality was significantly higher in most age categories, with the exception of those under 30, where it was lower or the same in 2020.

**20. C) Compare these current client satisfaction metrics to those from the previous year**
Primary data collection/analysis involves collecting and analyzing data that does not already exist. While often more expensive and time-consuming than obtaining and analyzing secondary, or existing, data, it can provide key insights about the specific population or topic of interest.

# ● REFERENCES

Aday, L. A., & Cornelius, L. J. (2011). *Designing and conducting health surveys: A comprehensive guide.* John Wiley & Sons.

Bartholomew, L. K., Parcel, G. S., & Kok, G. (1998). Intervention mapping: A process for developing theory and evidence-based health education programs. *Health Education & Behavior, 25*(5), 545–563. https://doi.org/10.1177/109019819802500502

Bensley, R. J., & Brookins-Fisher, J (Eds.). (2009). *Community health education methods: A practical guide* (3rd ed.). Jones and Bartlett.

Centers for Disease Control and Prevention. (2014). Assessment & planning models, frameworks & tools. *U.S. Department of Health and Human Services.*http://www.cdc.gov/stlt-publichealth/cha/assessment.html

United States Census Bureau. (2022). *List of household surveys.* https://www.census.gov/programs-surveys/surveyhelp/list-of-surveys/household-surveys.html

Gilmore, G. D. (2012). *Needs and capacity assessment strategies for health promotion and health education* (4th ed.). Jones and Bartlett.

Glanz, K., Rimer, B. K., & Viswanath, K. (Eds.). (2008). *Health behavior and health education: Theory, research, and practice.* John Wiley & Sons.

Gordon, R. S., Jr. (1983). An operational classification of disease prevention. *Public Health Reports, 98*(2), 107–109.

Green, L. W., & Kreuter, M. W. (1992). CDC's planned approach to community health as an application of PRECEDE and an inspiration for PROCEED. *Journal of Health Education, 23,* 140–147. https://doi.org/10.1080/10556699.1992.10616277

Harris, M. (2010). *Evaluating public and community health programs.* Jossey-Bass.

Office of Disease Prevention and Health Promotion. (n.d.). Healthy People 2030. *U.S. Department of Health and Human Services.* https://health.gov/healthypeople

Centers for Disease Control and Prevention. (n.d.). About the National DPP. *U.S. Department of Health and Human Services.* https://www.cdc.gov/diabetes/prevention/about.htm

Centers for Disease Control and Prevention. (2013). *Community needs assessment.* https://www.cdc.gov/globalhealth/healthprotection/fetp/training_modules/15/community-needs_pw_final_9252013.pdf

Issel, L. M. (2004). *Health program planning and evaluation: A practical, systematic approach for community health.* Jones & Bartlett Learning.

McKenzie, J. F., Neiger, B. L., & Thackeray, R. (2016). *Planning, implementing & evaluating health promotion programs: A primer.* Pearson.

Morgan, A., & Ziglio, E. (2007). Revitalizing the evidence base for public health: An assets model. *Promotion & Education, 14*(2 Suppl), 17–22. https://doi.org/10.1177/10253823070140020701x

Kretzmann, J., & McKnight, J. P. (1996). Assets-based community development. *National Civic Review, 85,* 23–29. https://doi.org/10.1002/ncr.4100850405

Robinson, K. L., Driedger, M. S., Elliott, S. J., & Eyles, J. (2006). Understanding facilitators of and barriers to health promotion practice. *Health Promotion Practice, 7*(4), 467–476. https://doi.org/10.1177/1524839905278955

Trotter, R. T., Needle, R. H., Goosby, E., Bates, C., & Singer, M. (2001). A methodological model for rapid assessment, response, and evaluation: The RARE program in public health. *Field Methods, 13*(2), 137–159. https://doi.org/10.1177/1525822X0101300202

World Health Organization. (2017). *EPHO5: Disease prevention, including early detection of illness*. http://www.euro.who.int/en/health-topics/Health-systems/public-health-s ervices/policy/the-10-essential-public-health-operations/epho5-disease-prevention, -including-early-detection-of-illness2

# Area of Responsibility II: Planning[1]

## ▶ INTRODUCTION

This chapter will cover how to plan health education and promotion programs. Health education specialists use skills every day that help with the planning, implementation, and evaluation of programs. This chapter focuses on the planning of health education programs and interventions. It includes an overview of how to engage priority populations, how to define desired goals and objectives, determine the strategies for selecting or developing effective strategies and/or interventions, develop the plans and materials needed for successful implementation and delivery, as well as identifying and addressing both facilitators and barriers to implementation.

## ▶ ENGAGING PRIORITY POPULATIONS AND RELEVANT STAKEHOLDERS IN THE PLANNING PROCESS[2]

To be successful in the implementation of health education and promotion programs you must engage priority populations. Additionally, identifying successful engagement strategies during planning can allow program staff and stakeholders to add value to current and future efforts.

There are several strategies and stakeholders that should be considered during the planning process. Start with outreach to stakeholders such as other health program staff, supervisors, managers, and local community health workers. Engagement strategies may include social media, phone, text messaging, mailings, word of mouth, flyers, and many more (Pullen-Smith et al., 2008). You might find valuable partnerships with community-based organizations (CBOs), faith-based organizations, volunteers from the community, and trusted stakeholders who can help to recruit community members to engage in the planning process.

Potential engagement models and strategies that should be considered are community-based participatory approaches such as Lay Health Advisor Models (Shelton et al., 2015), Community Coalitions (Butterfoss et al., 1996), and Community Advisory Boards (Brieland, 1971; Evans et al., 2018). Lay Health Advisor Models—sometimes called peer educators, promoters,

---

[1] The Eight Areas of Responsibility for Health Education Specialists are copyright of the National Commission for Health Education Credentialing, Inc. (NCHEC).

[2] Competency 2.1 Engage priority populations, partners, and stakeholders for participation in the planning process, copyright of the National Commission for Health Education Credentialing, Inc. (NCHEC).

community health navigators, or peer outreach workers—promote health and education to community members who share similar backgrounds, including social, economic, linguistic, and cultural. Lay health advisors are typically trained to work with community members to promote health among traditionally underserved groups and communities.

Community coalitions can act as a tool for planning and implementing health promotion programs. A **community coalition** often comprises key community stakeholders from schools, policy makers, law enforcement, and community professionals from relevant publication and community organizations with a joint interest in education and preventing the health outcomes of interest. Key areas of a coalition to consider include leadership potential, ability to participate in shared decision-making, strength of communication, and willingness to collaborate across members of the coalition, as well as establishing a climate of collaboration, participation, and communication which often leads to great satisfaction across coalition members (Butterfoss et al., 1996).

**Community advisory boards** are typically made up of stakeholders from the local community with the purpose of informing and assisting the health promotion team with planning, implementation, evaluation, and often, research components of a project. The advisory board can help with supporting the project team by identifying issues and concerns of the community, providing feedback on the program development steps, and advising on how the program impacts the community throughout the entire project from beginning to end. In the next section, we will describe some of the key stakeholders and partners to consider inviting to be a part of your strategies to identify priorities for health education and promotion program planning.

## ▶ IDENTIFY PRIORITIES OF POPULATIONS, PARTNERS, AND OTHER STAKEHOLDERS

Perhaps one of the most important steps in program planning and evaluation is to identify all community partners and stakeholders who will be involved in the program or intervention. Typically, **stakeholders** are individuals or groups from a specific community or agency that share a common goal, value, or identity. Stakeholders often represent the "who" and "what" of your intervention (Wholey et al., 2010).

A **community-based organization (CBO)** is a public or private nonprofit organization (such as a church or health agency) that represents the needs of a community or a segment of a community. CBOs are often engaged in meeting the human, educational, environmental, or public safety needs of a community (National Network of Libraries of Medicine, 2016).

Input from community-based partners and stakeholders will support program development and evaluation. Consider the practical and political implications of having community stakeholders involved in the planning and evaluation phases. Engaging multiple stakeholders can help to facilitate collaborative efforts among populations, partners, and other stakeholders, and to identify priority areas.

The focus should be on what the community needs and wants and to elicit input on the plan. Key questions should be:

- What outcome(s) does the community find most important?
- How can a particular health problem be reduced or improved?

It is vital that health educators ask members of the community about their perceptions of the problem and about potential causes of the problem. This is an opportunity to use data from the needs assessment or collect additional data on a particular health problem. This should be informed by a literature review and additional data on the health problem. In order to collect data on the particular health problem, you may choose to use a community survey, phone interviews, focus groups, in-depth interviews, or conduct a landscape or environmental scan (Community Tool Box, 2016; Rowel et al., 2005).

**Focus groups** are small panels of persons (8–10 people) who are knowledgeable or can share a perspective on a specific topic or health problem (Rossi et al., 2004). An experienced facilitator should lead the group in a discussion in order to identify important themes or descriptions of the panels' experiences and perspectives.

Collecting primary data from the community will support program planning (Centers for Disease Control and Prevention [CDC], 2016a). Primary data can provide you with insights into local beliefs, attitudes, and knowledge of the health problem. It can also aid in identifying social norms, obtaining community buy in, and determining the priorities of the community. It may also help identify potential ideas for the interventions.

## ▶ OBTAIN COMMITMENTS TO PARTICIPATE IN HEALTH EDUCATION/PROMOTION

**Community-based participatory research** (CBPR) is a method used to bring together community members to address a particular problem (Israel et al., 2005). CBPR involves community members in the design, implementation, evaluation, and reporting of the results of a research project or intervention (Warrick et al., 2005). Researchers function as facilitators and co-learners rather than experts. Health educators should consider this approach when developing community partnerships and to engage community members in the planning, implementation, and evaluation of health education and promotion programs.

## ▶ DEVELOP GOALS AND OBJECTIVES[3]

Program goals and objectives help health educators to achieve the desired outcomes, and they can help with establishing criteria and standards for how you will determine whether these outcomes are achieved (CDC, 2016b). **Goals** are broad statements about the long-term expectations or results of a health education program or intervention (CDC, 2015). Prior to establishing goals, specify and understand the potential causes of the health problem and target population(s) for your program.

Determine the prevention activities in terms of how your health education and promotion programs will bring about change to prevent or reduce illness and disease. A question to ask: Will your program focus on primary, secondary, or tertiary prevention strategies or a combination of one or more types of prevention? **Primary prevention** focuses on intervening before any of the illness or disease has occurred. For example, this might focus more on health behavior change, such as improving eating habits, quitting smoking, or increasing physical activity. **Secondary prevention** focuses on promoting screening to identify illness or disease before onset of any signs or symptoms of the illness. This might include biometric screenings, mammography, or other types of health screening. **Tertiary prevention** involves treatment and management of the illness or disease in order to slow or stop the progression. Examples include rehabilitation, medication adherence strategies, chemotherapy, or other treatments.

---

[3] Competency 2.2 Define desired outcomes, copyright of the National Commission for Health Education Credentialing, Inc. (NCHEC).

After deciding about the levels of prevention, it is now time to establish goals and objectives of your health education and promotion programs. Below we provide an example of how one might address this concern in an educational setting with students.

Goal examples: Reduce the number of students in the state ages 5 to 7 who are obese.

**Objectives** are statements that describe the achievable results and specify "who," "what," "where," and "how much" change will be achieved. Objectives can be established for process or outcomes. Objectives are more specific than goals and help to identify the steps necessary to reach a determined goal. Objectives are clear, specific, realistic, and measurable statements that include one indicator with a time frame.

Objectives examples: By 2015, 50% of children ages 5 to 7 will complete a school-based curriculum on physical activity and healthy eating.

SMART objectives were established to help identify the key activities of a program or intervention. **SMART** is an acronym used to address five important attributes of well-written objectives: **S**pecific, **M**easurable, **A**ttainable, **R**ealistic, and **T**ime-sensitive.

- **WHAT** activities will be completed?
- **WHY** is it important to complete these activities?
- **WHO** is responsible for completing the activities?
- **WHEN** will the activities be completed?
- **HOW** will these activities be completed?

Example: By (month/year), (X%) of target population will be able to state the guideline that adults need 30 minutes of physical activity most days.

---

**SMART Objectives:**
1. Specific: Includes the "who," "what," and "where."
2. Measurable: "How much" change is expected?
3. Attainable: Is it feasible to accomplish the desired results?
4. Realistic: Considers the resources, personnel, costs, and time frame.
5. Time-sensitive: Represents the "when" or time frame in which the activities will be completed.

---

*Source:* CDC (2016b), (2016c).

There are several different types of objectives that could be used based on the phase of your program, specific target population, and types of data that are being collected. Two main types of objectives are process and outcome.

**Process objectives** are used to monitor program implementation and provide data on how well the program is doing at reaching its target audience and intended activities.

**Outcome objectives** are used to monitor how well a program is doing at achieving the desired results of the program. Outcome objectives are used to describe the effect of the program on the specific health problem. Often these outcome objectives are further distinguished by identifying short-term (i.e., changes in attitudes, knowledge, and skills), intermediate (changes in behavior, norms, and policy), and long-term objectives (i.e., changes in a specific health problem).

Objectives are different from activities. **Objectives** are the clear and specific statements that describe the results that will be achieved and measure progress towards the program goals. **Activities** are the tasks or events that take place as part of a program.

> **Example:**
> **Activity:** Educate parents on physical activity guidelines for children.
> **SMART short-term objective:** By 2015, 75% of children ages 5 to 7 will be aware of the need for 30-minutes of physical activity every day.

Objectives may also be specific to type of activities being implemented in a program, such as behavioral, environmental, learning, and administration objectives. Environmental objectives have to do with influences on the environment. Behavioral objectives focus on behaviors or actions that help to address the health problem and goals of the program. Learning objectives have to do with change in knowledge necessary to reach the program goal. Finally, administrative (process) objectives have to do with key tasks that are accomplished by the program staff that are necessary for implementing the program. Examples of process objectives might include: the number of trainings completed, number of staff trained, number of sites reached, or number of hours training. Process objectives are measured throughout the life of a program and include data from logbooks, inventories, and staff reports (CDC, 2016).

# ▶ DEVELOP A VISION AND MISSION STATEMENT

Having a vision and mission statement can be used to guide your health education or promotion program. A mission statement describes the *what* and *why* of your program (Community Tool Box, 2016). Mission and vision statements are similar in that they both describe the larger picture or broad goals of your program.

## VISION STATEMENT

Vision statements represent the aspirations of your program. A vision statement should be a short phrase that describes the long-term and broad goals of your program. It should represent the governing principles of your program and the greater community or population you are targeting. It should be easily understood and communicated by others and inspire others to action.

Examples of vision statements:

"Create the healthiest nation in one generation."—American Public Health Association

"A healthy world through health education."—Society for Public Health Education (SOPHE)

"Every kid healthy, active and ready to learn."—Action for Healthy Kids

## MISSION STATEMENT

A mission statement should be short, about one sentence, describe the overall outcomes your program/intervention is trying to achieve, and make a broad statement about the program's key goals.

Examples of mission statements:

"Serve as the national focus for developing and applying disease prevention and control, environmental health, and health promotion and health education activities designed to improve the health of the people of the United States."—CDC

"Improve the health of the public and achieve equity in health status."—American Public Health Association

"To provide global leadership to the profession of health education and health promotion and to promote the health of society."—SOPHE

"To mobilize school professionals, families and communities to take actions that lead to healthy eating, physical activity and healthier schools where kids thrive."—Action for Healthy Kids

# ▶ DETERMINE EFFECTIVE HEALTH EDUCATION AND PROMOTION STRATEGIES AND/OR INTERVENTIONS[4]

It may seem overwhelming at first when you are trying to identify the most useful strategies for planning health education and promotion programs and interventions. Consider a model or theory to guide you in the program planning and development process, especially when trying to create or modify strategies that will to lead to an evidence-based program and intervention.

Theories and models provide a road map and strategies for identifying health problems, developing appropriate interventions, and evaluating the successes of the interventions. Theory can inform the planner's thinking during all of these stages, offering insights that translate into stronger programs. Theory can also help to explain the dynamics of health behaviors, including processes for changing them, and the influences of the many barriers and facilitators that affect health behaviors, including the social and physical context. Theory can also help planners identify the most suitable priority populations, methods for fostering change, and outcomes for evaluation.

---

**Theories versus Models**

Theory: A set of interrelated constructs, definitions, and statements that present a systematic view of events or situations by specifying the relationships among variables, with the sole purpose of explaining and predicting the events or situations.

Model: Often draws upon several theories in order to better understand a health problem in a specific setting or context.

---

Source: Glanz, K., Rimer, B. K., and Viswanath, K (Eds.). (2008). *Health behavior and health education: Theory, research, and practice* (4th ed.). Jossey-Bass.

# ▶ PRECEDE/PROCEED MODEL

The PRECEDE/PROCEED model is a community-oriented, participatory model aimed at developing successful community health education and promotion programs and interventions (Glanz & Rimer, 2005).

---

**PRECEDE/PROCEED Model**

Five Phases of the PRECEDE Model:
**Phase 1:** Social diagnosis
**Phase 2:** Epidemiologic diagnosis
**Phase 3:** Behavioral and environmental diagnosis
**Phase 4:** Educational and organizational diagnosis
**Phase 5:** Administrative and policy diagnosis
Four Phases of the PROCEED Model:
**Phase 6:** Implementation
**Phase 7:** Process evaluation
**Phase 8:** Impact evaluation
**Phase 9:** Outcome evaluation

---

[4] Competency 2.3 Determine health education and promotion interventions, copyright of the National Commission for Health Education Credentialing, Inc. (NCHEC).

The PRECEDE/PROCEED model can guide you in the planning process and provide structure for developing the health education program. The PRECEDE/PROCEED model also highlights the importance of participatory approaches to ensure community and stakeholder involvement (Glanz & Rimer, 2005).

PRECEDE/PROCEED incorporates a multi-level evaluation, which we will discuss in Chapter 5. It includes processes for monitoring and adjusting your evaluation approach. Since the model focuses on program planning, it also provides some flexibility and allows for the adapting of content and methods that are most relevant to your program/intervention and the particular needs and circumstances of your community and stakeholders.

*PROCEED* stands for Predisposing, Reinforcing, Enabling Constructs in Educational/ Environmental Diagnosis, and Evaluation. **Predisposing factors** may motivate or be responsible for a given behavior, such as knowledge, attitudes, beliefs, values, or other factors that impact readiness to change. This also includes identifying potential barriers for health education programs. **Enabling factors** include those influences that enable an individual to act on a specific behavior, such as resources, services, supportive policies, and other facilitators of health education programs. **Reinforcing factors** are influences that encourage repeated behaviors or incentivize continued practice of the behavior. Reinforcing factors include social support, rewards, praise, or symptom relief.

**Phase 1:** Social diagnosis—Multiple sources of data collection that focus on better understanding the perceived needs of a community (i.e., focus groups, key informant interviews, surveys, and participant observation).

**Phase 2:** Epidemiologic diagnosis—Typically involves secondary health outcome data or data that describes a health problem and potential causes of the health problem. This data is often used to develop program goals and objectives.

**Phase 3:** Behavioral and environmental diagnosis—This includes data on internal and external factors that influence behavior and the environment. Often this data may come from literature reviews or theories that can be used to explain behavior.

**Phase 4:** Educational and organizational diagnosis—This includes data on individual, interpersonal, or community-level theories that can identify and describe the key determinants of health behaviors. These areas are typically classified as predisposing, reinforcing, or enabling factors.

**Phase 5:** Administrative and policy diagnosis—This involves a diagnosis of strategies and data from the administrative and policy-level sources. It included data collected from previous steps, including availability of resources and organizational policies that may impact program implementation.

*PROCEED* stands for Policy, Regulatory, and Organizational Constructs in Educational and Environmental Development. These steps focus on program implementation and evaluation.

**Phase 6:** Implementation—This phase involves processes for implementing and evaluating the health education program.

**Phase 7:** Process evaluation—This phase focuses on program fidelity or the extent to which a program is being implemented as it was designed and planned.

**Phase 8:** Impact evaluation—This examines changes in predisposing, enabling, and reinforcing factors and the influence of a program on the desired behavioral and environmental changes.

**Phase 9:** Outcome evaluation—This final phase examined whether the program has affected the desired health problem.

**Program planning** involves identifying the needs, priorities, potential root causes of health problems, facilitators (i.e., available and needed resources), and barriers to achieving the objectives and overall goals of the program. Prior to developing your health education and promotion programs, consider any potential barriers and facilitators that could influence the success and uptake of your health education program or intervention. Health educators may want to select a model to aid them in the planning process. While there are many different models out there, finding the right one may be a challenge if you don't know about the key elements of your program.

Remember that there may not be a perfect model for your program or planning process. Often, health educators will have to either use a model that does not align that well, or they may choose to use parts of the model or a combination of several planning models to best meet the needs of their program, community, and stakeholders. This is why the first phase of the needs assessment (described in Chapter 2) is so important and can help with identifying your priorities, partners, and stakeholders.

It is important to include community members and stakeholders in your program planning, development, implementation, and evaluation. Inclusive or participatory approaches will help to ensure that the program addresses the community's concerns.

**Strategy** is a general approach to preventing an overall health problem. For instance, a physical activity intervention for childhood obesity might involve multiple strategies, such as teaching parents about healthy cooking and encouraging parents to incorporate physical activity into family activities.

**Interventions** involve a set of activities or strategies to prevent a specific health problem and address the factors that contribute to the problem. For example, a physical activity intervention might involve a school-based curriculum and social norms campaign to encourage physical activity.

**Programs** involve a group of strategies or interventions to address a health problem. For example, a physical activity program for adolescents might include a school-based curriculum and a home visit to obtain support from parents.

**Logic Model** is a flowchart that provides an organized way of understanding the key elements of a program (Wholey et al., 2010). Logic models include resources, inputs, activities, outputs, objectives, and short-term, intermediate, and long-term outcomes. Logic models are also helpful in identifying factors that may be outside of the health educators and program staffs' control. Logic models are especially helpful in identifying the causal links among the key elements of the program that lead to the desired program outcomes. Logic models will be discussed more in Chapter 5 page 82.

# ▶ DEVELOPING YOUR PLANS AND MATERIALS FOR HEALTH EDUCATION AND PROMOTION IMPLEMENTATION AND EVALUATION[5]

## LEARNING STRATEGIES

Health educators are often in the position of teaching and training adults. Adult learners have distinct characteristics. First, and most important, they must be shown respect, just as you would want to be respected by someone who was teaching you something. Adult learners should be thought of as autonomous and self-directed. Introduce yourself as a facilitator, not a teacher, and involve the participants as much as possible in the design of the educational

---

[5] Competency 2.4 Develop plans and materials for implementation and evaluations, copyright of the National Commission for Health Education Credentialing, Inc. (NCHEC).

materials or training. Second, adult learners come with a life-time of experience and knowledge that you as a teacher or trainer can use to help put your information into context. In some situations, they may know more about a certain aspect of the situation you are talking about—the neighborhood, what it is like caring for someone with a disease, the frustration of trying to get a law changed year after year. Recognize their experience and encourage participants to share their experiences with you and each other.

Adult learners usually approach a learning situation with a goal, so you need to plan your trainings to clearly state what the goals and objectives of the trainings or educational sessions will be (we'll discuss setting learning objectives below). It is important that adult learners understand how, and need to see how, new information is relevant and practical to them either personally or professionally.

Think for a moment how you learn best. Do you like to learn things by reading them? Hearing them? Doing them? Most of us have a preference, but science tells us that a mix is probably best. We retain different amounts of information depending on how it is presented or how we interact with it. Just sitting in a lecture? You may only remember 5% of what you hear. Have to teach someone something? You're likely to remember almost all of the information afterword. Selecting the appropriate method to the material—we don't all have to know everything well enough to be able to teach it to someone—is part of the health educator's job. Some instructional strategies include:

- Lecture
- Discussions
- Role play
- Brainstorming
- Reflective writing
- Group problem-solving
- Icebreakers
- Quizzes
- Games
- Simulations
- Tabletops
- Case studies

## LEARNING DOMAINS

There are generally considered to be three domains of learning:

- Cognitive: mental skills (*knowledge*)
- Psychomotor: manual or physical skills (*skills*)
- Affective: growth in feelings or emotional areas (*attitude or self*)

**Bloom's Taxonomy** is often used when writing learning objectives for educational or training purposes (Figure 3.1). It focuses on the cognitive, or knowledge domain. If you need to write learning objectives, you will select a word from the taxonomy to describe what you want the learner to be able to do by the end of the training or class. Be sure to select appropriate levels of objectives for the audience, topic, and setting of the class.

While on the subject of learning, it is worthwhile mentioning that, when teaching adults, you should keep in mind the comfort and access to learning of people in the room. Rooms should be neither too hot nor cold. Rooms should have adequate light, and the older the

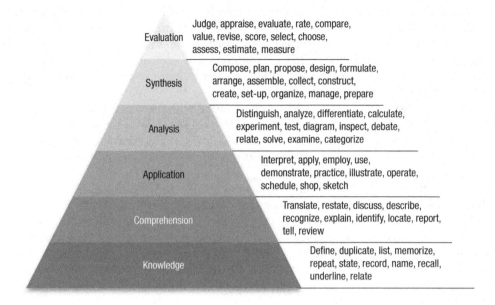

**Figure 3.1** Bloom's taxonomy

adults, the more light may be needed. Consider access for a range of disabilities—how would someone who was deaf or blind interact with the material you are presenting? Is the building wheelchair accessible? Will the room have what you will need to instruct your learners, such as whiteboards or audio/visual equipment? What will you do if some of the equipment fails? What is the plan if there is a medical emergency during the session? Planning for these things beforehand will pay off in the long run.

## ▶ PILOT PROGRAMS

As you near the end of the planning process, there are still several issues to consider. The first is integrating heath education into other programs that may already exist in the community. In planning health education activities, you may discover that there are clear relationships to other programs to which your health education activities can be linked. Perhaps during your planning phase, you have made some of these connections, and you are going to implement your health education in connection with existing programs in communities, universities, worksites, or school systems. This is also the time to think about addressing factors that will affect implementation. **Pilot programs** are a way of testing a program or a health education material in its entirety in a limited location. This allows the health educator to discover and fix problems before a large-scale launch, or decide to scrap the project altogether before investing substantial resources in a full-scale launch. If an intervention is going to be expensive, is brand-new, has very limited evidence behind it, or covers a wide geographical area, consider a pilot program.

## ▶ CONCLUSION

The time you have spent planning, developing program goals and objectives, and piloting projects will pay off as you move to implement your program. As your program moves into the implementation phase, which we will discuss in the next chapter, we will see how we can use tools such as logic models and timelines to make sure the program activities go as planned, adapt to new information and changing information and environments, and respond to the realities of working in the real world. Chapter 4 will review Competency Area III: Implementation of Health Education/Promotion Programs.

1. The level of effort of a task, who is assigned to a task, and when a task starts and stops is information that can be found in a:

   A. Logic model
   B. Budget
   C. Gantt chart
   D. SWOT (strengths, weaknesses, opportunities, and threats) analysis

2. In a community with 4,000 deaths in a year, eight deaths are due to drowning. Which of the following values represent this data in a manner that allows comparison with other populations of interest?

   A. 0.0020
   B. 2.0%
   C. 20 per 1,000
   D. 20 per 100,000

3. A health educator in a health department wants to start a campaign to test lead levels in children in an underserved neighborhood with a high percentage of immigrants. What would be a good first step?

   A. Print brochures in English and Spanish listing testing hours and sites
   B. Hold two community meetings
   C. Talk with local gatekeepers to find out what baseline community needs and concerns are
   D. Mandate lead testing

4. When planning an ethnographic study and trying to find the most appropriate site to conduct the research, which is the least important factor for a researcher to consider?

   A. Participants requesting the location
   B. The researcher's ability to control the setting
   C. The relevance of the site for the research interest
   D. The researcher's ability to gain access to the site

5. When planning quasi-experimental designs, which is an accurate statement of their characteristics?

   A. Quasi-experimental designs can control for confounding factors
   B. Quasi-experimental designs use randomization
   C. Quasi-experimental designs create the same strength of evidence as experimental designs
   D. Quasi-experimental designs don't use control groups

## 1. C) Gantt chart

A Gantt chart identifies who is assigned to a task, when a task begins and ends, and the intensity or level of effort a task may require in order to aid planning and monitor implementation.

## 2. D) 20 per 10,000

8/4,000 = 20/10,000. 10,000 is a more standard denominator of comparison.

## 3. C) Talk with local gatekeepers to find out what baseline community needs and concerns are

Before holding community meetings, printing materials, or certainly passing rules or laws, it makes sense to speak to community gatekeepers to get the lay of land to see where the community is with respect to the issue.

## 4. B) The researcher's ability to control the setting

The relevance of the site for the research interest, the ability of the researcher to gain access, and the acceptability of the site to the population of interest are all important factors in site selection. The researcher's ability to control the dynamics setting is not only not important, it is undesirable in qualitative research and runs counter to the ethos of conducting ethnographic research.

## 5. A) Quasi-experimental designs can control for confounding factors

Quasi-experimental designs use control groups but do not randomize participants/settings and do not generate the same strength of evidence that experimental designs do. However, they can control for confounding in the design by ensuring that control group is as similar to the treatment group in all relevant variables.

6. Requiring that children under the age of 2 ride in rear-facing car seats is an example of what kind of prevention program?

   A. Health communication
   B. Health marketing
   C. Health policy
   D. Health education

7. Looking at Figure 3.2, what conclusion can you draw?

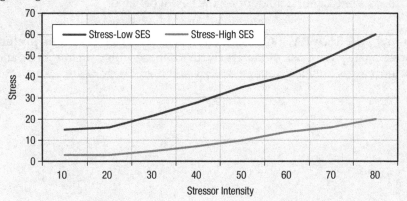

**Figure 3.2** Stress by SES

   A. Personal stress is associated with an inability to adopt a health behavior
   B. Social stress is associated with an inability to adopt a health behavior
   C. Personal stress and social stress interact in the adoption of health behaviors
   D. It is impossible to draw a conclusion from the figure

8. Looking at the risk of preterm birth associated with maternal body mass index (BMI) in the Figure 3.3, which of the following is true?

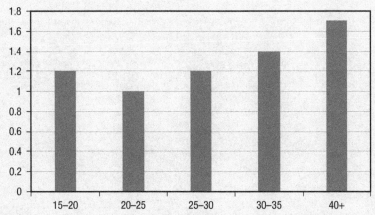

**Figure 3.3** Risk of preterm birth associated with mother's body mass index risk ratio

   A. There is no association between BMI and preterm birth
   B. Low BMI and very high BMI do not differ in risk of preterm birth
   C. The increase in risk associated with low BMI is 40%
   D. Both low and high BMI are associated with increased risk of preterm birth

## 6. C) Health policy

Health policy is the field that is involved with laws, rules, and regulations that relate to health promoting and disease prevention behaviors.

## 7. B) Social stress is associated with an inability to adopt a health behavior

When social stress is high, the percentage of people adopting the health behavior is low, regardless of personal stress. When social stress is low, the percentage of people adopting the behavior is high, regardless of personal stress levels. Therefore, social stress, rather than personal stress, is associated with not adopting the health behavior.

## 8. D) Both low and high BMI are associated with increased risk of preterm birth

The data shows an increased risk of preterm birth for those with both low, high, and very high BMI, but the increase is only the same in the low and high categories.

9. A health educator at a health department is using the data from Figure 3.3 to help plan a program to reduce preterm births. If the health educator was using the PRECEDE-PROCEED model of program planning, this data would be used during what phase of the process?

   A. Social diagnosis
   B. Epidemiologic, behavioral, and environmental diagnosis
   C. Educational and ecologic diagnosis
   D. Administrative and policy diagnosis

10. A health educator, in trying to reduce preterm births by helping pregnant women to maintain a healthy weight during pregnancy, develops the Healthy Moms, Healthy Babies program. The health educator wants to gather together a group of pregnant women and medical personnel to advise her on specific medical issues related to pregnancy and the feasibility and acceptability of introducing particular activities to pregnant women as part of the program. Which type of group should the health educator convene to ensure that the best decisions are being made?

    A. Delphi panel
    B. Focus group
    C. Advisory committee
    D. Task force

11. A health educator is planning a program to increase the number of tweens who receive their first human papillomavirus (HPV) vaccinations. Which of the following is the best example of a SMART (Specific, Measurable, Attainable, Realistic, and Time-sensitive) objective for the program?

    A. The program will increase HPV vaccination
    B. The program will increase HPV vaccination by 15%
    C. By the end of Year 2, 100% more tween patients at Really Good Doctor's Office will be vaccinated for HPV than at baseline
    D. By the end of Year 2, 10% more tween patients at Really Good Doctor's Office will be vaccinated for HPV than at baseline

12. "The mission of the Healthy Moms, Healthy Babies program is to ensure that all babies born in Anytown, USA, get the best start to life by helping moms have full-term pregnancies" is an example of a:

    A. Goal statement
    B. SMART (Specific, Measurable, Attainable, Realistic, and Time-sensitive) objective
    C. Mission statement
    D. Vision statement

13. "Healthy Moms, Healthy Babies: Ensuring that all babies are born full-term and ready to thrive" is an example of a:

    A. Goal statement
    B. SMART (Specific, Measurable, Attainable, Realistic, and Time-sensitive) objective
    C. Mission statement
    D. Vision statement

### 9. B) Epidemiologic, behavioral, and environmental diagnosis
This data falls under Phase 2 of PRECEDE-PROCEED, as it is epidemiologic data.

### 10. C) Advisory committee
An advisory committee, or advisory board, would be the best way to get the combination of expert and lay advice that the health educator needs. A Delphi panel is used to establish consensus when there is little definitive evidence and opinion is important. Focus groups are not appropriate in this case as you want an ongoing group to provide input. A task force is designed to work toward change, not simply provide guidance and advice.

### 11. D) By the end of Year 2, 10% more tween patients at Really Good Doctor's Office will be vaccinated for HPV than at baseline
SMART Goals need to be Specific, Measurable, Attainable, Realistic, and Time-sensitive. The difference between C and D is that a 100% increase in vacination rate, while desirable, is not attainable or realistic (unfortunately).

### 12. C) Mission statement
Mission statements describe the "reason for being" of the program in one sentence.

### 13. D) Vision statement
Vision statements describe the long-term change that the program hopes to bring about eventually. They may represent an idealized vision of the world, or something to "shoot for" with the recognition that it is unlikely to ever be fully realized.

14. A health educator is responsible for planning an intervention to deal with the depression and mental health issues employees face as identified by a health risk assessment in a medium-sized nonprofit organization. Which of the following is the most appropriate program to address these problems?

A. "Lunch-and-learn" educational programs
B. Stress management programs
C. An Employee Assistance Program (EAP)
D. An Alcoholics Anonymous program

15. Replacing some parking spaces at work with covered bike storage is what kind of intervention?

A. Persuasive
B. Environmental
C. Community mobilization
D. Social

16. Which one is true about focus groups?

A. The results are generally not shared beyond the research staff
B. Individual focus groups yield the richest information when participants are as diverse as possible so that a range of opinions are represented
C. A focus group usually lasts 1 to 2 hours
D. The same kinds of data can generally be obtained from either focus groups or individual interviews

17. The Short Physical Performance Battery (SPPB) measures lower extremity strength (Figure 3.4). Which of the following is NOT true?

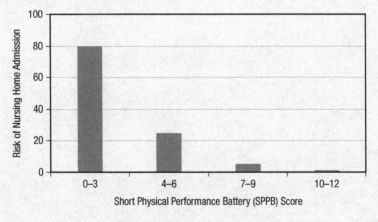

**Figure 3.4** Risk of nursing home admission by Short Physical Performance Battery (SPPB) Score

A. Low scores increase nursing home admissions
B. The SPPB is a good tool for predicting risk of nursing home admissions over 12 months
C. Improving lower extremity strength might reduce nursing home admissions
D. The relationship between SPPB performance and nursing home admissions is linear

### 14. C) An Employee Assistance Program (EAP)

An EAP is a voluntary, work-based program, paid for by the employer, that offers free (to the employee) confidential assessments, short-term counseling, referrals, and follow-up services to employees who have personal and/or work-related problems. EAPs address issues such as alcohol and substance abuse, stress, grief, family problems, and psychologic disorders.

### 15. B) Environmental

By making it harder to park a car and easier to store a bike, you have changed the environment.

### 16. C) A focus group usually lasts 1 to 2 hours

Most focus groups last between 60 and 120 minutes. It takes about that long to orient the group, do introductions, set the ground rules, and explore the topics at hand. Food and child-care is often provided for in-person focus groups.

### 17. D) The relationship between SPPB performance and nursing home admissions is linear

The relationship between SPPB performance and nursing home admission is closer to exponential than linear.

18. A researcher found a statistically significant relationship between variable X and variable Y at the 0.05 alpha level. What does this mean?

A. 95 out of 100 times, the results are true

B. There is a 5% chance there is a real relationship

C. A researcher can be 90% sure the results of the study are a reflection of the population if random sampling was used

D. The researcher's study is poorly designed

19. A health educator is planning a program that would be better informed if he conducted in-depth interviews with key stakeholders of the program and gatekeepers in the community of interest. Which of the following is true about conducting in-depth interviews?

A. Interviewers should avoid using probes or follow-up questions

B. Interviewers must read each question exactly as they appear on the interview questionnaire

C. Interviewers can reveal their personal background to the interviewee to build trust and rapport

D. Interviewers should agree with the participant's opinion and take their side

20. What type of prevention is chemotherapy an example of?

A. Primary

B. Secondary

C. Tertiary

D. Quaternary

**18. A) 95 out of 100 times, the results are true**
A 0.05 alpha level means that 5 out of 100 times the results would not occur naturally.

**19. C) Interviewers can reveal their personal background to the interviewee to build trust and rapport**
It is not unusual for interviewees to ask questions of the interviewer. Disclosing personal information (appropriately) "levels the field" and often helps generate trust. Also, refusing to answer participant's questions may generate suspicion.

**20. C) Tertiary**
Chemotherapy is a type of intervention designed to reduce harm from cancer, and therefore a tertiary prevention.

# REFERENCES

Brieland, D. (1971). Community advisory boards and maximum feasible participation. *American Journal of Public Health, 61*(2), 292–296. https://doi.org/10.2105/AJPH.61.2.292

Butterfoss, F. D., Goodman, R. M., & Wandersman, A. (1996). Community coalitions for prevention and health promotion: Factors predicting satisfaction, participation, and planning. *Health Education Quarterly, 23*(1), 65–79. https://doi.org/10.1177/109019819602300105

Centers for Disease Control and Prevention. (2016a). *A framework for program evaluation.* http://www.cdc.gov/eval/framework/index.htm

Centers for Disease Control and Prevention. (2016b). *Developing program goals and measurable objectives.* https://www.cdc.gov/std/Program/pupestd/Developing%20Program%20Goals%20and%20Objectives.pdf

Centers for Disease Control and Prevention. (2016c). *Planning, implementing, and evaluating an intervention—An overview.* http://www.cdc.gov/violenceprevention/pdf/chapter1-a.pdf

Community Tool Box. (2016). *Chapter 2: Other models for promoting community health development.* http://ctb.ku.edu/en/table-of-contents/overview/models-for-community-health-and-development/healthy-cities-healthy-communities/main

DiClemente, R. J., Salazar, L. F., & Crosby, R. A. (2013). Evaluating theory-based public health programs: Linking principles to practice. In K. Glanz, B. K. Rimer, & K. Viswanath (Eds.), *Health behavior theory for public health: Principles, foundations, and applications* (pp. 287–308). Jones & Bartlett Publishers.

Eder, M. M., Evans, E., Funes, M., Hong, H., Reuter, K., Ahmed, S., Calhoun, K., Corbie-Smith, G., Dave, G., DeFino, M., Harwood, E., Kissack, A., Kleinman, L. C., & Wallerstein, N. (2018). Defining and measuring community engagement and community-engaged research: Clinical and translational science institutional practices. *Progress in Community Health Partnerships: Research, Education, and Action, 12*(2), 145–156. https://doi.org/10.1353/cpr.2018.0034

Evans, E., Funes, M., Hong, H., Reuter, K., Ahmed, S., Calhoun, K., ... & Wallerstein, N. (2018). Defining and measuring community engagement and community-engaged research: Clinical and translational science institutional practices. *Progress in Community Health Partnerships: Research, Education, and Action, 12*(2), 145-156.

Glanz, K., & Rimer, B. K. (2005). *Theory at a glance: A guide to health promotion practice* (2nd ed.). National Cancer Institute.

Glanz, K., Rimer, B. K., & Viswanath, K. (Eds.). (2008). *Health behavior and health education: Theory, research, and practice* (4th ed.). Jossey-Bass.

Israel, B. A., Eng, E., Schulz, A. J., Parker, E. A., & Satcher, D. (2005). *Methods in community-based participatory research for health.* Wiley.

National Network of Libraries of Medicine. (2016). *Community based organization defined.* https://nnlm.gov/sea/funding/cbodef.html

Pullen-Smith, B., Carter-Edwards, L., & Leathers, K. H. (2008). Community health ambassadors: A model for engaging community leaders to promote better health in North Carolina. *Journal of Public Health Management and Practice, 14*(6), S73–S81. https://doi.org/10.1097/01.PHH.0000338391.90059.16

Rossi, P. H., Lipsey, M. W., & Freeman, H. E. (2004). Expressing and assessing program theory. *Evaluation: A Systematic Approach, 7*, 133–168.

Rowel, R., Moore, N. D., Nowrojee, S., Memiah, P., & Bronner, Y. (2005). The utility of the environmental scan for public health practice: Lessons from an urban program to increase cancer screening. *Journal of the National Medical Association, 97*(4), 527.

Shelton, R. C., Dunston, S. K., Leoce, N., Jandorf, L., Thompson, H. S., Crookes, D. M., & Erwin, D. O. (2015). Predictors of activity level and retention among African American lay health advisors (LHAs) from The National Witness Project: Implications for the implementation and sustainability of community-based LHA programs from a longitudinal study. *Implementation Science, 11*(1), 1–14. https://doi.org/10.1186/s13012-016-0403-9

Warrick, C., Culica, D., Quill, B. E., Spears, W., & Vojvodic, R. W. (2005). Community development and public health. *Reinventing Public Health: Policies and Practices for a Healthy Nation, 6*, 237-284.

Wholey, J. S., Hatry, H. P., & Newcomer, K. E. (2010). *Handbook of practical program evaluation.* John Wiley & Sons.

# Area of Responsibility III: Implementation[1]

## ▶ INTRODUCTION

Once needs have been assessed and programs have been planned, it is time for them to be implemented. Implementation is the time when "the rubber hits the road," and as a health educator you get to see how all that needs assessment, audience research, goal setting, theory selection, message development, and program planning is going to work in the real world. In a classroom setting, teaching occurs, tests are given, and teaching assistants are trained. In a community or worksite setting, you may be launching websites or social media campaigns, spending the day at local barbershops giving flu shots and taking blood pressures, or swapping out junk food for fruit at workplace vending machines, all while making sure that the program is going according to plan and everyone involved knows what they are supposed to do and when. While a thorough job in the assessment and planning stages will serve you well, there is still a lot to learn and do in this phase.

## ▶ IMPLEMENT A PLAN OF ACTION

According to McKenzie et al. (2016), there are five phases of implementation:

1. Adopting the program.
2. Identifying and prioritizing tasks.
3. Establishing a management system.
4. Enacting the plan.
5. Ending or sustaining the program.

In the following section, we discuss what is needed to optimize program implementation.

The first step in implementation is actually more planning. As you have probably noticed by now, health educators spend a lot of their time planning! First, let us define what we mean by implementation. **Implementation** is putting our plans into action—launching and running the program. In a training program, that could be recruiting for and holding trainings for the people who will be running the program. At a hospital, we might launch a flu shot campaign and spend 6 weeks promoting the availability of flu shots through posters, emails, lunch and learns, and incentive programs. In a community setting, we might plan to improve physical activity rates by improving awareness through local media, partnering with parks to provide daily walking tours, promoting low-cost classes held at community centers, or working with schools to increase the time students spend at recess. All of those are examples of program implementation. Developing and following a plan for implementation—an action plan—will help keep things running smoothly. The action plan should include a step-by-step accounting of everything that needs to happen, who is responsible for it, any materials or items necessary, and what to do if something goes wrong.

---

[1] The Eight Areas of Responsibility for Health Education Specialists are copyright of the National Commission for Health Education Credentialing, Inc. (NCHEC).

## ASSESS READINESS FOR IMPLEMENTATION[2]

While considerable effort may have already gone into the development of a program, now is the time to assess how ready your program is for implementation. Look at the plan you created. What needs does it have in terms of resources—staffing, funding, partners, equipment, and so on? This is the time to make sure that the goals and objectives you set are achievable with the resources you have. For instance, if you planned on holding educational sessions at a local library and you discover now that the conference room is being renovated, you need to rethink your plans before you go any further. Likewise, if in the planning process you have now added additional parts of the intervention, such as increasing access to screenings by keeping the clinic open 2 additional hours 3 days a week, you need to make sure that you have the funding and the staff to make that happen. If not, could volunteers, donations, or in-kind services fill the gap, or do you need to seek additional funding? Many programs run into trouble because they do not have the resources they need when they need them, so take time at the beginning to make sure you have considered all aspects of resources before proceeding.

## TRAINING FOR IMPLEMENTATION

Many implementation errors and challenges can be prevented by proper training. While we often think of training our populations of interest (such as providing cooking classes or car-seat installation sessions), program staff should be trained on program implementation as well. The more complex the implementation, the more important training becomes. One document that you should develop for training is a **Manual of Procedures (MOP)**. A MOP is a document, often in the form of a handbook or binder, that details a project's or study's operations and procedures and facilitates consistency in implementation and data collection across project participants and sites. When questions about procedure arise, the MOP is the guidebook to which the implementor can refer for answers.

For example, say you are implementing an evidence-based teen pregnancy prevention program in a school system. The program has been previously demonstrated to be effective as written, which means it needs to be delivered as written to have the greatest chance of success. Teachers need to be trained, therefore, on all the components of the program, with an emphasis on delivering the training as it is written. Too often in such implementations, program drift occurs—the delivered materials move away from the intervention as planned, either deliberately or due to carelessness. Those delivering the intervention need to be trained on the importance of delivering the intervention as intended. During training, it is a good time to ask for feedback on challenges or concerns that those delivering the intervention might have. In this example, teachers may note that in their school system, classes are 50 minutes long, rather than the 55 minutes the curriculum allows. Training can be a time to make minor adjustments to the implementation to suit local needs. Likewise, if those implementing the program are uncomfortable with certain topics, training can help them overcome their anxieties and convince them of the need to deliver the program as intended.

Another important part is training project implementers on how and when to report changes, deviations, or problems that occur during implementation. Developing a structure for reporting these issues will allow project managers to respond quickly to any problems. Using our previous example of the teen pregnancy prevention program, say it was scheduled after school on Wednesdays for 8 consecutive weeks. If students miss weeks 4 and 5 due to snow days and attendance was very low on week 7 due to illness, program managers need to

[2] Competency 3.1. Coordinate the delivery of intervention(s) consistent with the implementation plan, copyright of the National Commission for Health Education Credentialing, Inc. (NCHEC).

be alerted in real time so they can make adjustments. Otherwise, 3 of the 8 weeks of curriculum will have been missed and the project will be unlikely to meet its objectives.

A final aspect of training to consider is that implementing the training is, in and of itself, a program implementation and, as such, must follow all of the steps of an implementation. Regardless of who the audience of your intended program may be, if the staff or volunteers you are training consist of adults (which is likely), you must consider the needs of adult learners in your training plans.

Adults learn best when:

1. They understand why they are being trained.
2. They can choose ways to learn that work best for them.
3. The training is experiential or hands-on.
4. The timing is right for them.
5. The process is positive and encouraging.
   —Adapted from The University of Washington at Green Bay (n.d.)

We'll talk more about training in Chapter 8.

## ▶ IMPLEMENT PROGRAM[3]

### COLLECT BASELINE DATA

As you can likely anticipate, evaluation is critical to a comprehensive health education program. If the purpose of evaluation is to find out what changes a program made, then we must know what the situation was BEFORE the program was launched. This is the time to collect baseline data—both qualitative and quantitative—so we have an accurate BEFORE picture. Quantitative and qualitative data are reviewed in Chapter 2, so please refer to them for a more in-depth discussion of the methods available to you as a health educator.

As a health educator, you will have to decide whether you need to collect **primary** or **secondary** data at this stage. **Primary data** are those data you collect yourself. These could come from surveys, focus groups, in-depth interviews, observations of current behavior, sales receipts, and so on. The key is that this is the data your program has specifically collected to serve in understanding what is going on in the primary, secondary, or tertiary audience or the setting in which an intervention is to take place. Primary data can be costly and time consuming to collect, analyze, and interpret depending on the size and scope of your project, but the benefits can be enormous because they can answer the needs of your program and give you insight as to the specifics of your population and environment. Remember, primary data gathering can occur in many forms and at many levels of depth. If you do not have the resources for a sophisticated data collection effort, well-placed key informant interviews and some community meeting observations, for example, may give your valuable insight for not much investment of resources. During the initial response to COVID-19, for instance, some health educators were asked to create videos to be shown in waiting rooms for Federally Qualified Health Centers explaining basic nonpharmaceutical interventions to prevent transmission, such as masks and physical distancing. Because time was of the essence, and due to the challenges of conducting in-person research, program staff attended executive committee meetings with clinic leadership and spoke with clinical staff to understand what kinds of questions and misinformation patients had, what behaviors they were seeing in the clinic (incorrect mask use, etc.), as well as average

---

[3] Competency 3.2. Deliver health education and promotion interventions, copyright of the National Commission for Health Education Credentialing, Inc. (NCHEC).

length of time patients were spending in waiting rooms. Such information, while quickly gathered, was crucial in the implementation of the project.

**Secondary data**, on the other hand, are the data collected for another purpose that might be useful or applicable for your intervention. Examples of secondary data sources are the Behavioral Risk Factor Surveillance System (www.cdc.gov/brfss), U.S. Census Bureau (https://data.census.gov/cedsci/), and the National Center for Health Statistics (www.cdc.gov/nchs). A listing of many publicly available secondary data sets is available at www.cdc.gov/stltpubl ichealth/cha/data.html. **Indicators** are a kind of secondary data that can be used to compare rates of, or trends in, health outcomes or determinants. The advantage of using secondary data is that it has been collected and often analyzed for you, dramatically reducing your cost and time investment. The challenge, of course, is that it was collected to meet somebody else's needs and may not fully answer all the questions for your program. As a health educator, it is part of your job to balance the desire for program-specific information with the budgetary and time constraints of your project to come up with baseline data that tell you what you need to know to implement your program well.

Collecting baseline data, be it primary, secondary, or a combination, will be a critical building block for your evaluation plan. We will talk about evaluation in Chapter 5, but once you have made your evaluation plan, you will have to implement the baseline data collection before you launch your program so you know what the conditions were before the implementation began.

## LAUNCH THE PROGRAM

Before implementing your program, use this checklist to ensure you are ready for a successful launch:

- Are all partners prepared for the launch?
- Have we invited reviewers, gatekeepers, and other stakeholders who have been involved in the program development?
- Have we trained project staff and spokespeople?
- Are program-related services (such as hotlines, screening tests, materials) in place?
- Is there a media plan in place?
- Are all program-related materials ready?
- Do we have enough program-related materials to begin the program and respond to media/public inquiries?
- Do we have a way to get more materials if they are necessary?
- Is there a monitoring plan in place?
- Are other health-related professionals in the community aware of the program and ready to respond to their clients if they are asked about it?

*Source*: Adapted from National Cancer Institute, 2002.

If you can complete the earlier checklist, it is time to launch our program! There are several possibilities for how to do this, each with their own plusses and minuses. Many times, a health educator starts by launching a **pilot program**. Pilot programs are, by design, small, and may address only one audience or location. The goal of a pilot program is to work out the "kinks" and see what works or what does not work in the implementation. Positive aspects of a pilot program are that they give you a real-world, yet manageable, idea of how the audience thinks and feels, and what it will do with your program. If mistakes are made or pieces of the intervention are inadequate or redundant, you can find this out while there is time and money to correct problems. You will likely learn a lot about the differences between a program on paper and conducting one in a real setting—information that can help you revise and improve your program. Are people receptive to what you are trying to do? Do they understand your materials? Do they feel safe working with the program? Do they believe what you are telling them? Does the intervention take longer than you predicted to have a desired result? The downside of a pilot program is that it costs money, takes time, and the things you learn in your pilot may not be generalizable to your full implementation. Still, a pilot can be a very valuable tool and should be employed if at all feasible.

If you have piloted your program and made revisions, you may move to a phase-in approach to implementation. A phase-in approach is the middle ground between your pilot and full implementation. Perhaps you offer it to all audiences in one geographic area, or one type of audience across your geographic areas. Or perhaps you start with one part of the implementation and save other parts for later. A phase-in approach also has the benefit of simplifying what you are doing so it is easier to spot problems and correct them. But in the case where something is urgently needed, such as information on an emerging infectious disease, it is unlikely that you will be able to take the time.

The full implementation, whether it happens after a pilot or phase-in implementation, is your final stage of implementation. Next, you will begin monitoring your implementation to ensure that it is going according to plan.

## ▶ MONITORING IMPLEMENTATION[4]

Often overlooked in favor of evaluation, monitoring is a critical piece of the implementation process and should be planned with the implementation from the beginning. **Monitoring** has two specific purposes: to make sure that the implementation happens as it was planned and to identify any unforeseen or unexpected issues or events that may affect the project's implementation or outcomes. Monitoring is "keeping your fingers on the pulse" of the implementation so you can quickly respond with corrections to your implementation as needed.

Issues you need to periodically assess include:

- Are activities being completed at scheduled times?
- Are your intended audiences being reached?
- Which materials are being used more successfully? Less successfully?
- Are there activities that need to be expanded or eliminated?
- Are you within budget?

One framework that can be helpful in the implementation and monitoring phase (as well as in the planning phase) is the RE-AIM framework (Glasgow et al., 2019). RE-AIM stands for:

- Reach
- Effectiveness
- Adoption
- Implementation
- Maintenance

---

[4] Competency 3.3. Monitor implementation, copyright of the National Commission for Health Education Credentialing, Inc. (NCHEC).

**Table 4.1** Sample selected RE-AIM project metrics

| RE-AIM Dimension | Description of Metrics Used to Evaluate Each Dimension | Data Source |
|---|---|---|
| REACH | Number and description of clients (≥18) who participate in screening, are eligible for project, and enroll<br><br>Number of participants who participate in activities and complete project (retention) | Baseline survey data, risk test<br><br>Sign-in sheets, project records, midpoint survey |
| EFFECTIVENESS | Changes in dietary intake and physical activity from baseline to 6 months follow-up<br><br>Percentage of clients who engage with screenings, classes | Baseline, midpoint survey<br><br>Project records, evaluation data<br><br>Staff interviews, project records |
| ADOPTION | Number and type of partners who participate in program;<br><br>Volunteer and staff feedback and satisfaction | Baseline, mid-point data, project records, key informant interviews<br><br>Staff survey, key informant interviews |
| IMPLEMENTATION | Project costs<br>Adherence to and consistency in the delivery of intervention<br><br>Adaptations required and made during project period<br><br>Media coverage | Project/grant records<br>Project log, key informant interviews, site visits<br><br>Project log, key informant interviews, site visits<br><br>Press clippings file |
| MAINTENANCE | Project alignment with organization's mission and business model<br><br>Plans/recommendations for program adaptation and sustainability | Key informant interviews<br>Key informant interviews, midpoint survey, staff survey |

Table 4.1 shows sample RE-AIM metrics and data sources for a fictional project to improve nutrition and physical activity in a community-based setting. By monitoring these aspects of the program implementation, program staff can ensure that the program is proceeding the way it was intended and make corrections or adjust to new circumstances when warranted. Metrics for program evaluation (which are discussed in the Chapter 5) are also clearly articulated.

Program management should maintain an open-door policy and attitude around program implementation and monitoring, and MOPs should be updated regularly to reflect lessons learned in the implementation. All program staff, participants, and stakeholders should be encouraged to bring concerns to the attention of the program management team as soon as possible, so that concerns can be addressed before they reduce the likelihood of program effectiveness. Likewise, things that are going well in implementation should also be noted so they can be scaled in more effective ways.

## PROJECT TIMELINES

Project timelines, often known as Gantt charts, are a way of helping to plan and monitor how a project is implemented. They help visualize what tasks must be done before another task can be completed, and what steps are necessary to bring a project to fruition. They are an excellent monitoring tool to provide the user the ability to look at the chart on any given day and see if the project is running on time, what has been completed, and what lies ahead. There are several project management software solutions for creating project timelines, or they may be created in a spreadsheet program like Excel. Exhibit 4.1 shows a template created in Excel for a 10-week, simple program that requires material development and evaluation. The more complex an intervention, the more complex the project timeline is likely to be. Using color and subheadings to distinguish among different phases or areas of responsibility can help keep complex timelines more manageable (Exhibit 4.1).

| Task | Who is responsible? | Week 1 | Week 2 | Week 3 | Week 4 | Week 5 | Week 6 | Week 7 | Week 8 | Week 9 | Week 10 |
|---|---|---|---|---|---|---|---|---|---|---|---|
| **Administration** | | | | | | | | | | | |
| Task 1 | | ▓ | | | | | | | | | |
| Task 2 | | ▓ | | | | | | | | | |
| Task 3 | | | ▓ | | | | | | | | |
| Task 4 | | | ▓ | | | | | | | | |
| Task 5 | | | | ▓ | | | | | | | |
| **Material Development** | | | | | | | | | | | |
| Task 1 | | | | | | | | | | | |
| Task 2 | | | | | | | | | | | |
| Task 3 | | | | | | | | | | | |
| Task 4 | | | | | | | | | | | |
| Task 5 | | | | | | | ▓ | | | | |
| Task 6 | | | | | | | | ▓ | | | |
| Task 7 | | | | | | | | | ▓ | | |
| Evaluation | | | | | | | | | | | |
| Task 1 | | | | | | | | | | ▓ | |
| Task 2 | | | | | | | | | | | ▓ |
| Task 3 | | | | | | | | | | | |

**Exhibit 4.1** Example of a project management spreadsheet.

# ▶ CONCLUSION

This chapter provided an overview of strategies and competencies needed to successfully implement health education programs and interventions. It is important to consider the process of implementation, the application theories of behavior change, cultural competence, training, and monitoring of implementation. In Chapter 5, you will review Area IV: Evaluation and Research.

1. Which action do you NOT take in the literature review of a proposal?

   A. Build an argument for the study
   B. Demonstrate the relevance of the study
   C. Describe how you will measure variables in your study
   D. Present epidemiologic data related to the issue under study

2. For which of these tasks is a reference manager such as EndNote NOT helpful?

   A. Permit you to cite what you write easily
   B. Change your references from APA style to AMA format quickly
   C. Decide which citations should be used for justifying your study
   D. Store all your references in one place

3. A health educator is implementing a pilot project where rapid response teams are available to go into communities that have been affected by gun violence and provide grief counseling and support. If the program shows positive outcomes, it will be expanded. To ensure fidelity to intervention and track lessons learned during the implementation, the health educator should develop a MOP, which stands for:

   A. Manual on Places
   B. Manual of Plans
   C. Manual of Procedures
   D. Manual of Priorities

4. All of the following types of interventions may pose barriers to the dissemination of evidence-based programs, except:

   A. Interventions that lack flexibility
   B. Interventions that account for user's needs and preferences
   C. Interventions that have a high degree of technical sophistication
   D. Interventions that have garnered limited organizational support

5. The time to consider the sustainability of an implementation of a program or study is:

   A. In the planning stages
   B. At the beginning of implementation
   C. At the halfway mark
   D. At the end of the first round of funding

6. All of the following can be used to monitor implementation and progress toward goals and objectives, except:

   A. Gantt chart
   B. Program Evaluation and Review Technique (PERT)
   C. Critical Path Method (CPM)
   D. Evidence-Based Medicine Reviews (EBMR)

## 1. C) Describe how you will measure variables in your study
Describing how you will measure variables in your study will be discussed in the methods section.

## 2. C) Decide which citations should be used for justifying your study
A reference manager can be a very helpful tool for organizing your work, but it cannot help you make decisions about what is valuable to your work.

## 3. C) Manual of Procedures
A Manual of Procedures, or MOP, is a document that contains policies, roles and responsibilities, procedures, and protocols for an implementation.

## 4. B) Interventions that account for user's needs and preferences
Interventions that consider beneficiaries' needs and preferences are more likely to be successfully disseminated than ones that are not developed considering these aspects.

## 5. A) In the planning stages
Program sustainability must be considered from the beginning of the planning stages. If the program is not sustainable on its own, what partners or stakeholders can be brought in to help improve sustainability?

## 6. D) Evidence-Based Medicine Reviews (EBMR)
Gantt chart, PERT, and CPM are all methods of monitoring program implementation. EBMR is a collection of databases that offer evidence-based programs such as the Cochrane Systematic Reviews.

7. Which of the following would be the correct order of steps when implementing a worksite health promotion program to reduce back injuries?

   A. Introduce the program to management, promote health risk assessment (HRAs), introduce the program to employees, and schedule trainings
   B. Introduce the program to management, introduce the program to employees, promote HRAs, and schedule trainings
   C. Introduce the program to employees, introduce the program to management, promote HRAs, and schedule trainings
   D. Promote HRAs, introduce the program to management, introduce the program to employees, and schedule trainings

8. All of the following are reasonable approaches to take when the demand for a project exceeds project resources, except:

   A. Screening or wait-listing participants on a preset criteria
   B. Referring those not selected for an intervention to community resources
   C. Selecting those most at need for the intervention
   D. Selecting only one demographic group to serve for convenience of data collection

9. The objective, "By the end of this training, the participant will be able to filter a gallon of water and list five items to pack in an emergency kit," addresses:

   A. Knowledge and skills
   B. Attitudes and knowledge
   C. Skills and behavior
   D. Skills and attitudes

10. Immediately following a training, participants were given a posttest to assess knowledge. This represents what type of evaluation?

    A. Formative
    B. Process
    C. Outcome
    D. Summative

11. When developing trainings for adult learners, the most important principle for the instructor to keep in mind is:

    A. Make the training as easy as possible
    B. Make the training relevant to the audience's jobs or personal lives
    C. Be funny to keep the audience's attention
    D. Explain your credentials for teaching so they will recognize your authority

12. RE-AIM stands for:

    A. Reach, Evaluate, Adaption, Implementation, Maintenance
    B. Reach, Effectiveness, Adaptation, Implementation, Maintenance
    C. Reach, Evaluate, Adoption, Implementation, Maintenance
    D. Reach, Effectiveness, Adoption, Implementation, Maintenance

*(See answers next page.)*

## 7. B) Introduce the program to management, introduce the program to employees, promote HRAs, and schedule trainings

First management, and then employees at large, need to know about the program before they are likely to buy into the idea of taking an HRA. Once the results of the HRA are in hand, the health educator can begin scheduling trainings.

## 8. D) Selecting only one demographic group to serve for convenience of data collection

When project resources have to be rationed, care must be taken to do so in an ethical matter. Providing a wait-list, community referrals, and prioritizing needs are all ethical approaches if done thoughtfully and considered a priori. Selecting one demographic group for the convenience of the organization when there is high community demand is likely unethical.

## 9. A) Knowledge and skills

Filtering a gallon of water is a skill, but being able to list five items is a knowledge-level domain.

## 10. C) Outcome

A posttest measures the short-term outcome of the training—that is, what level of knowledge participants had after the training.

## 11. B) Make the training relevant to the audience's jobs or personal lives

Most adult learners respond well to training when they can see that it has a tangible relevance to their lives, either personally or professionally.

## 12. D) Reach, Effectiveness, Adoption, Implementation, Maintenance

These five components create the RE-AIM Framework. Effectiveness can also be Efficacy.

13. Project costs are generally accounted for in which component of the RE-AIM model?

   A. Reach
   B. Implementation
   C. Maintenance
   D. Program costs are not important in RE-AIM

14. A health educator at a college student health center wants to ensure that an evidence-based sexual assault prevention program is being implemented with fidelity. Which of the following actions would they take?

   A. Count the number of attendees at each session
   B. Employ a pre-/postsurvey to check for knowledge gain
   C. Observe sessions to ensure the planned material was being covered
   D. Monitor sexual assault statistics

15. A program at a local hospital for people recently diagnosed with type 2 diabetes needs to teach the participants how to monitor their blood sugar. Which would be the most effective set of strategies?

   A. Lecture followed by brainstorming
   B. Lecture followed by demonstration
   C. Demonstration followed by practice
   D. Practice followed by role play

16. Preparing for a program launch may include all of the following activities except:

   A. Analyzing survey data
   B. Requisitioning space and supplies
   C. Hiring and training staff
   D. Producing materials

17. _____ is an activity or set of activities used by program staff to try out a program on a small group of participants before the implementation of a program.

   A. Pilot test
   B. Promotion
   C. Planning
   D. Pretest

18. A health educator needs to collect baseline data prior to implementation with very limited time and budget. Which of the following would be a reasonable option for primary data?

   A. Stratified focus groups representing significant populations in the area
   B. Key informant interviews
   C. Literature review and review of local vital statistics
   D. Representative survey of the community

### 13. B) Implementation
Implementation refers to the project's fidelity to key parts of the program or plan, including consistency of delivery as intended and the timing and cost of the intervention.

### 14. C) Observe sessions to ensure the planned material was being covered
Fidelity means that the program is being delivered as intended. Observing that the material as being covered as planned is a one strategy to ensure fidelity.

### 15. C) Demonstration followed by practice
Certainly, the program could contain some component of lecture and role play, but for skill acquisition, demonstration and practice would be the most effective strategies.

### 16. A) Analyzing survey data
In preparation for implementation, you might hire and train staff, issue requests for proposal (RFPs) and award funds, or produce written or online materials. Analyses of survey data, while potentially helpful for developing or evaluating programs, would come earlier in the planning process.

### 17. A) Pilot test
A pilot test is done as a sort of "dry run" for the project. It comes after the planning process and may include promotion and pretests.

### 18. B) Key informant interviews
In a very limited time and budget situation, key informant interviews may serve as the least resource intensive primary baseline data. Holding focus groups with different populations and a representative survey would yield richer data, but be more costly and time consuming. Literature reviews and vital statistics are secondary data.

19. Evaluation from pilot test data finds that videos explaining how vaccines work to produce antibodies in people were confusing and contained language and concepts not familiar to the population. This feedback came from what type of evaluation?

A. Formative
B. Process
C. Impact
D. Summative

20. Based on the information in Question 19, what strategy does the health educator need to employ to improve the videos before implementing the program fully?

A. Social marketing
B. Media literacy
C. Tailoring
D. Plain language

### 19. B) Process
Because the pilot has launched and the program is running, albeit in limited form, the staff is gathering information about how it is performing. This then makes feedback gathered process feedback.

### 20. D) Plain language
Plain language principles, including avoiding jargon and employing visuals and analogies, should be employed to ensure the greatest number of people possible will understand.

# REFERENCES

Glasgow, R. E., Harden, S. M., Gaglio, B., Rabin, B., Smith, M. L., Porter, G. C., Ory, M. G., & Estabrooks, P. A. (2019). RE-AIM Planning and evaluation framework: Adapting to new science and practice with a 20-year review. *Frontiers in Public Health*, 7, 64. https://doi.org/10.3389/fpubh.2019.00064

McKenzie, J. F., Neiger, B. L., & Thackeray, R. (2016). *Planning, implementing, and evaluating health promotion programs: A primer* (7th ed.). Pearson.

National Cancer Institute. (2002). *Making health communication programs work: A planner's guide.* U.S. Department of Health and Human Services, Public Health Service, National Institutes of Health. https://www.cancer.gov/publicati ons/health-communication/pink-book.pdf

University of Washington at Green Bay. (n.d.). *Creating trainings using adult learning principles.* https://www.uwgb.edu/UWGBCMS/media/ Continueing-Professional-Education/files/Handout-0-Master-Handout-Adult-Learning -Principles-Participant-Handout.pdf

# Area of Responsibility IV: Evaluation and Research[1]

## ▶ INTRODUCTION

This chapter will provide an overview of strategies and competencies needed to design evaluations and research for health education programs and interventions. **Evaluation** is the systematic investigation of the relevance, quality, worth, and/or significance of a health education program or intervention (Rychetnik et al., 2004; Scriven, 1998). Evaluation allows you to assign "value" to a program's efforts. Program evaluation often considers the merit (or quality) of a program or intervention (Donaldson & Lipsey, 2006). It also helps define the program's worth (or value). For instance, sometimes evaluations determine the program's cost-effectiveness. Most often, evaluations seek to understand the process of implementing a program and the impact and outcomes a program had on a health problem. **Research** for health education programs and interventions, on the other hand, typically involves testing hypotheses and following the scientific method (Goodyear, 2018). The goal of research is to generate new knowledge that can help the health educator refine programs, understand how the educational and training activities work in real-world settings, and collect robust data to inform future research and programming.[2]

When developing an evaluation or research plan, health educators should ask themselves the following questions:

- What will be evaluated? For example, what are the outcome(s), problem(s), program(s), and context or environment?
- What aspects of the program should be considered when evaluating how well the program performs?
- What standards or targets must the program reach to be considered successful?
- What types of evidence will determine how well the program worked?
- Are the conclusions about the program's performance justified, and how do they compare to past evidence?
- How will the lessons learned from the evaluation be used to improve future programs and public health?

---

[1] The Eight Areas of Responsibility for Health Education Specialists are copyright of the National Commission for Health Education Credentialing, Inc. (NCHEC).

[2] Competency 4.1 Design process, impact, and outcome evaluation of the intervention, copyright of the National Commission for Health Education Credentialing, Inc. (NCHEC).

# ▶ TYPES OF EVALUATION

**Formative evaluation** involves using data from the Planning and Implementation (i.e., process evaluation) Areas of Responsibility to determine *fidelity* or whether a program is being implemented in the way it was designed. It also identifies ways to adjust program delivery (Rychetnik et al., 2004; Newcomer et al., 2015).

**Process evaluation** is a way to monitor and describe the steps necessary for program implementation. It can also aid in understanding the relationship between specific program elements and program outcomes (Saunders et al., 2005).

Process evaluations often help with determining fidelity. **Fidelity** is the extent to which the program elements were implemented as planned. Other questions that can be answered include the dose delivered and received, reach (e.g., targeting of participants or the extent to which the program was delivered to the intended audience), recruitment, and contextual factors (e.g., organizational issues and other barriers and facilitators.)

**Summative evaluation** examines how well the measures or judgments from the outcomes can be used to summarize and make conclusions about the program. It is often an important element of impact and outcome evaluations.

**Impact evaluation** refers to identifying the immediate or shorter-term effects of a program (Rychetnik et al., 2004). Examples include changes to knowledge, behavior, or attitudes. Often, this phase of the evaluation is focused on how well the program did in achieving its short-term outcomes.

**Outcome evaluation** involves measuring the overall outcomes and impacts of a program and measuring the long-term outcomes, such as morbidity or mortality, after the program has been completed (Rychetnik et al., 2004).

# ▶ DEVELOPING AN EVALUATION OR RESEARCH PLAN

Health educators must consider the best ways to evaluate the impact of their health education programs and interventions. The evaluation plan must align with the broader program or intervention goals and objectives. Additionally, it is vital to use existing research or evidence about the program or intervention as part of the evaluation or research plan.

For research designs, we recommend exploring whether an experimental, quasi-experimental, or nonexperimental design will best assess the goals/objectives. Plan to address institutional requirements and obtain human subjects research approval from an institutional review board before implementing any research components. Please see the U.S. Department of Health and Human Services, Office of Human Research Protections (https://www.hhs.gov/ohrp/), and CITI program on Human Subjects Research (https://about.citiprogram.org) for more details. Below we expand on potential research designs.

There are several different frameworks for evaluation plans. Incorporating a relevant theory to guide the evaluation plan may also be important. While we will not cover all of the frameworks, health educators should be aware of some of the most commonly used frameworks in public health. These include the Centers for Disease Control and Prevention's (CDC) Six-Step Framework for Program Evaluation; Reach, Effectiveness, Adoption, Implementation, and Maintenance (RE-AIM) framework (Gaglio et al., 2013); and the PRECEDE-PROCEED model (Green & Kreuter, 1999; please see Chapter 3). For this chapter, we will only focus on the CDC's Framework, given its wide use in evaluating health education and public health programs.

## CENTERS FOR DISEASE CONTROL AND PREVENTION SIX-STEP FRAMEWORK FOR PROGRAM EVALUATION

The CDC's Framework for Evaluation (Figure 5.1) involves a systematic six-step process to guide and summarize essential elements or develop a program evaluation plan (Davis, 2006). Public health practitioners and health educators often use this framework to guide program evaluations, and usually it is required for evaluating the impact of CDC-funded programs. Thus, health educators must become familiar with the six steps of this framework.

**Figure 5.1** Centers for Disease Control and Prevention (CDC) Framework for Evaluation

The six steps and primary activities (Koplan et al., 1999) are:

1. **Engaging stakeholders**: Includes meeting with stakeholders to involve them in the evaluation and gain consensus on the purpose of the evaluation.
2. **Describing the program**: Includes defining the overall mission, program objectives, and key outcomes of the program.
3. **Focusing on the evaluation design**: Includes the questions, data collection procedures, and protocols needed for the evaluation.
4. **Gathering credible evidence**: Includes collecting data, defining indicators, and ways to answer the evaluation questions.
5. **Justifying conclusions**: Includes data analysis, summarization, and interpretation of the data collected as part of the evaluation.
6. **Using and sharing lessons learned**: Includes reporting on and presenting results of the evaluation and discussing with stakeholders how the results will be used for program improvement and future program implementation, development, and evaluation.

## LOGIC MODELS

A logic model describes the sequence of events required to make a change by identifying the critical program elements (Koplan et al., 1999). Elements that are connected within a logic model may vary but generally include:

- **Inputs/resources:** the information and resources being used to develop or implement a health education program (e.g., funding, staff, and stakeholders)
- **Activities:** the actions or changes undertaken to implement the program
- **Outputs:** the results of the actions or changes, such as changes in policies, practices, or systems
- **Outcomes:** the short-term, intermediate, and long-term changes in the audience, such as changes in behaviors, attitudes, knowledge, and disease rate (e.g., morbidity and mortality)
- **Indicators:** the specific, observable, measurable characteristics of changes that demonstrate progress toward outcomes or impact

Please see an example of a program logic model in Figure 5.2.
Please see the following website for examples of logic models and further details: https://www.cdc.gov/eval/tools/logic_models/index.html

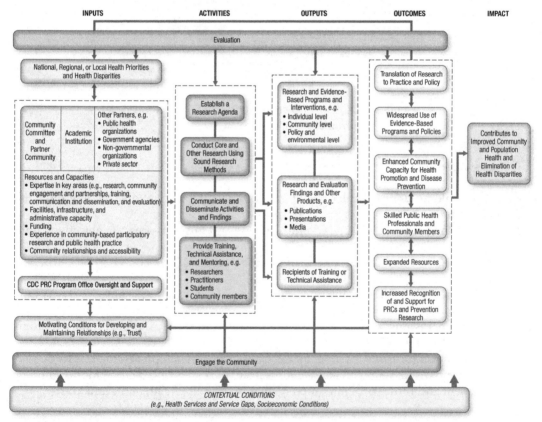

**Figure 5.2** Logic Model for the Prevention Research Centers Program at the Centers for Disease Control and Prevention (CDC)

Note: Last Revision July 14, 2008 (4)

**What Logic Models Can Do for You (Adapted from CDC Office of Oral Health, 2017)**

Logic models link program inputs (i.e., resources) and activities to program products and outcomes (i.e., goals) while communicating the logic (theory) behind the program and its rationale for existing. Logic models can be used to:

1. Identify the products and short-term, intermediate, and distal outcomes for your program.
2. Link outcomes to each other and to program activities using the identified logic/theory/model for your program (illustrate cause and effect).
3. Incorporate findings from research and demonstration projects.
4. Select indicators to measure outcomes depending on the stage of your program's development.
5. Demonstrate why the program is important and its fundamental purpose.
6. Depict what intermediate outcomes/products must occur before distal outcomes are evident.
7. Make mid-course adjustments and improvements in your program.
8. Become a common reference point for staff, stakeholders, constituents, and funding agency.

A logic model will assist you in communicating the underlying theory (logic) that you have about why your activities are the right solution to the identified problem.

Varying methods can display logic models. Some read left to right, others top to bottom with intermittent circles and squares, while others follow a winding path; all are designed to demonstrate the link (logic/theory) of what leads to what. What are the connections between resources, activities, products, and outcomes? Why and how will your program work?

Logic models often provide the needed synthesis of your program to convey why your program is important and the logic behind why you expect it to succeed. A logic model is an iterative tool, providing a framework to revisit throughout program planning, implementation, and evaluation.

# ▶ RESEARCH AND STUDY DESIGNS

Research plays an integral part in creating the evidence base for public health, health education, and promotion programs (CDC Office of Oral Health, 2017). Depending on the purpose of your study or research, different research designs and methods, such as quantitative, qualitative, or mixed methods, will be needed. Below, we will overview the key terms, methods, and research designs health educators often use when conducting research.

# ▶ STUDY DESIGNS

Typically, health education and public health studies fall into two categories: (a) descriptive or analytical (observational) or (b) experimental studies (Rychetnik et al., 2004). Observation studies involve investigators collecting, recording, describing, and analyzing data on subjects and testing potential relationships. Observational studies do not involve directly manipulating a variable (Rychetnik et al., 2002). Study designs include: Cross-sectional (one point in time), ecological, cohort, case-control (retrospective), longitudinal (prospective), and hybrid studies.

**Descriptive studies** aim to identify the qualities or distribution of variables. Key components of descriptive studies:

■ Examine phenomena as they naturally occur
■ Describe levels or characteristics of several variables, or aspects of one variable

- Can often identify an independent and a dependent variable
- Utilize quantitative data
- Often compare two populations
- Generalization is often not a goal

---

**Key Definitions**

**Quantitative research** tests a hypothesis based on concepts (variables) within a theory. It also involves quantifying numbers (e.g., "how many") or depicting the results of a program based on the data collected and analyzed.

**Qualitative research** seeks to understand social phenomena by exploring and interpreting the meanings that people attach to, and use to make sense of, their experiences of the social world. Qualitative research data often comprises descriptions, written notes from observations, and an examination of patterns or meaning from these descriptive words.

**Sample size** is the number of observations or participants in a study.

**Data analysis** involves analyzing data in some way to impose meaning.

**Quantitative data analysis** enables researchers to organize, interpret, and communicate numeric information.

**Qualitative data analysis** typically takes the narrative form or written words to organize, provide structure to, and elicit meaning, usually in the form of themes that emerge from coded data.

**Problem statement** describes the need for the research or program through the development of an argument.

A **research question** is a question about the phenomenon that is being studied. Questions can be descriptive, relational, or causal.

A **hypothesis** is used to make a specific prediction about the answers to research questions. There are two approaches to conducting hypothesis testing: inductive reasoning (used to develop a hypothesis or theory) and deductive reasoning (tests a theory or hypothesis).

**Aims** or **objectives** are used to specify accomplishments to be achieved by a study or program. Please see more details in Chapter 3.

**Validity** refers to the degree to which something accurately represents a phenomenon.

**Internal validity** refers to research measurements reflecting the true intended concepts, or when an intervention is delivered in the way it was designed. There are several threats to internal validity in research studies, such as *attrition* (loss of participants), *testing effects, history* (events outside the study that impact results), *instrumentation concerns*, and *maturation* (subjects change during study due to getting older or other nonstudy related experiences).

**External validity** represents findings being generalizable to other groups, settings, or contexts.

**Measurement validity** is how accurately a measure or tool measures what it is designed to.

**Reliability** is the degree to which observations or measures can be replicated under the same conditions.

**Variables** are measured with numbers and analyzed with statistical procedures to determine whether predictive generalizations of a theory hold true.

**Dependent variable** is the outcome variable. Some examples might be measuring changes in knowledge, attitudes, behaviors, or a health condition, such as the risk of developing a disease or the severity of disease.

**Independent variables** are often the variables you manipulate, measure, and/or record. For example, you might want to explore how physical activity level (dependent variable) differs by age and gender or whether a health education program results in increasing physical activity levels.

---

**Analytic studies** investigate associations between variables and test hypotheses. These studies examine the association or relationship between two or more variables on a particular outcome (e.g., minutes of walking per day and weight loss). There is no manipulation of the independent variable. The researcher must be very careful about making any statements about cause and effect given the observational nature of these types of studies. Prospective studies look at relationships over time and retrospective studies look at past occurrences.

**Experimental studies** differ from observational studies in that the investigator has direct control over the dependent variable (Thompson et al., 2006).

Moreover, experimental studies involve some type of intervention and control by the investigators. For instance, the study might be a clinical trial testing the effects of a drug or exercise protocol. Experimental studies aim to establish causality.

There are two major types of experimental studies: (a) randomized control trials (RCT) or clinical trials and (b) community trials.

**Quasi-experimental design** includes controlled trials without randomization and a comparison group, but no control group. The limitations are that they cannot infer cause, variables are not controlled for, and participant selection bias may exist. Often, these are more feasible for health education and community-based intervention studies.

**Qualitative studies** can include qualitative description, ethnography, grounded theory, and critical theory. For instance, a common data collection approach for qualitative research might involve participant observation, in-depth interviews, or focus groups. Often, participants are selected based on convenience (nonprobability) or purpose (purposeful selection of specific individuals).

## ▶ DATA COLLECTION, MANAGEMENT, ANALYSIS, AND TYPES OF DATA[3,4]

Data collection and management are important tasks for health education specialists. Data can help you to determine how well your program worked and identify areas that you can improve in the future. It can also help with future planning and effectiveness studies.

Health education specialists should collect data in a structured manner. Both the people collecting the data and the study participants are constrained to ensure quality and consistency in what is asked and how the answers are reported to maintain objectivity, reduce biases, and facilitate data analysis (CDC Office of Oral Health, 2017; Thompson et al., 2006). Data collection procedures are implemented so that data are accurate, valid, and meaningful. It is also important to consider and identify existing instruments when evaluating outcomes because often they have already been shown to be valid and reliable. Examples of existing data sources can include surveys such as the Behavioral Risk Factor Surveillance Survey (BRFSS) and the Youth Risk Behavioral Surveillance System (YRBSS), CDC's WONDER online database, or data on current online activities of older adults through the Pew Internet and American Life Project at pewinternet.org. Often, health educators have to identify usable items from existing materials and use them as-is, adapt them to make them appropriate to a different population, or bring them up-to-date to modern usage or changing norms. Examples include adding  Instagram to social media offerings or updating demographic sections to provide more inclusive choices than simply "male" or "female." When designing new instruments, it is important to think about reliability (precision) and validity (accuracy). Consider whether the tool is sensitive, specific, appropriate to the objectives, can adequately capture the distribution of responses, and objectively measures the attribute or phenomenon.

---

[3] Competency 4.2 Design research studies, copyright of the National Commission for Health Education Credentialing, Inc. (NCHEC).

[4] Competency 4.3 Manage the data collection and analysis of evaluation and/or research data using appropriate technology, copyright of the National Commission for Health Education Credentialing, Inc. (NCHEC).

## CHOOSING DATA COLLECTION MEASURES

The measures (instruments or tools) you choose for data collection measures need to align with your research plan and the questions you are trying to answer. Additionally, health educators should consider the following:

- **Resources:** How many/much people, time, and money are available.
- **Availability and knowledge:** The availability of instruments and tools and the level of experience researchers have with these tools.
- **Cultural appropriateness:** Determining ifthe measures are culturally appropriate and reflect the priority population.
- **Norms and comparison groups:** Determining whether the instrument has norms based on the priority population for comparison.
- **Administration issues:** technology, training, and any other requirements needed for data collection.
- **Quality of measures:** Ensuring the reliablility, validity, and sensitivity of the instrument(s).

**Data collection procedures** describe the sequencing and specific procedures for data collection.

- Conditions that must be met for collecting data (e.g., where data collection will occur)
- Information to provide participants
- Procedures for use if participants become distraught or disoriented
- How to gather, record, and manage data

**Sampling** is the process of selecting cases to represent a population so that the conclusions made about the sample can potentially be representative of the priority population. A sample is ideally a subset of the priority population. Two major components of samples and sampling are representativeness and size (CDC Office of Oral Health, 2017).

**Sample representativeness** has to do with how well the sample aligns with the priority population. A representative sample is a sample that has key characteristics that are very closely aligned with the priority population. We often consider our sampling or selection of the sample to be either probability or nonprobability sampling.

**Sampling frame** is a list or map of sampling units in the population (e.g., individuals, households, communities, institutions) from which a sample may be selected.

A **probability sample** involves the random selection (i.e., like a flip of a coin) of characteristics of a population to try to mirror the priority population. A **nonprobability sample** does not involve the random selection of key characteristics from the population. Often in health education and community-based programs, we have to rely on volunteers or the available participants. Those who are available might not fully represent the population. A nonprobability sample is the weakest form of sampling, but it is the most-often-used sampling method in both evaluations and research because it is more convenient and feasible for projects with limited funding. Using a nonprobability sample often means you must be cautious about the interpretation of the findings as there is likely bias, especially in terms of whether findings will be generalizable to other groups.

**Sample size** is the recommended number of participants for a study given a set of parameters and the desired confidence level.

## TYPES OF DATA

**Nominal (categorical)** data classify variables into categories (e.g., gender, diagnosis, marital status, race/ethnicity). Numbers serve as codes to represent these categories, and they have no quantitative meaning (e.g., 1 = female; 2 = male).

**Ordinal (rank-order)** data sorts variables by ranking of an attribute. For example, you might rank level of exercise intensity (0 = sedentary; 1 = low; 2 = moderate; 3 = vigorous).

**Interval (continuous)** data can specify rank ordering on an attribute and assume equivalent distance between them, but its value does not indicate absolute magnitude (e.g., temperature, date of birth). There is equal distance between numbers on a scale, and data can be calculated meaningfully. Most clinical, social, and behavioral research instruments yield interval-level data.

**Ratio** data provides information on the intervals between objects and the absolute magnitude of the attribute because they have a meaningful zero (e.g., weight, blood pressure, pulse rate).

**Qualitative** data includes data from interviewing and observing study participants individually or as a group, as well as open-ended survey responses, documents, photographs, genealogies, maps, social network diagrams, diaries, journals, oral histories, and so on. The units of data collection include individuals and cultural systems. A longitudinal or cross-sectional length of time is used for data collection. You can record data using field notes, interview notes, observational notes, memos, logs, and recordings. You can then analyze data according to the research design and appropriate methods (e.g., content analysis, thematic analysis, concept mapping).

**Content analysis** involves the analysis of the content of narrative data to identify salient themes and patterns. Many different types of documents can be analyzed ranging from interviews, field notes, newspapers, social media content, etc. Researchers then make inferences from the texts.

**Thematic analysis** is the iterative identification of broad categories, patterns, or themes that emerge from the data. A theme is an abstract entity that conveys meaning and identity to a current experience. Thematic analysis often relies on examining the text data for similarities and differences.

**Concept mapping** involves constructing diagrams, maps, flowcharts, and organizational charts for organizing and representing data. These maps include circles, boxes, and/or connecting lines to visualize the relationships between the concepts.

**Data management** should involve a plan for how data will be stored; how it will be checked for accuracy as well as the protocols for cleaning and checking for errors; and the creation of a data dictionary or codebook that explains the variables, measures, and meaning or coding of the variables. Your data also needs to be kept secure, and storage is often easier when utilizing an electronic database.

## ▶ DATA ANALYSIS

Quantitative data analysis enables researchers to organize, interpret, and communicate numeric information. They may also use descriptive or inferential statistics to test potential relationships among the variables. Qualitative data analysis typically uses narrative or other subjective accounts to organize and elicit meaning in the form of themes based on the coded data (Table 5.1). Qualitative data analysis provides structure to, and elicits meaning from, data. Data collection and analysis often occur at the same time. Identifying salient concepts and themes often starts at the beginning of data collection. It is important to plan for the fact that qualitative data analysis takes time. There are no universal rules for analyzing qualitative data. The analytic data procedure varies depending on the qualitative research design (e.g., ethnography, phenomenology, grounded theory). Qualitative data analysis may involve content analysis, narrative analysis, discourse analysis, and thematic analysis (Trochim, 2006).

**Table 5.1** Differences between qualitative and quantitative data analysis

| Qualitative Analysis | Quantitative Analysis |
| --- | --- |
| Not always standardized | Standardized |
| Describes and explains a phenomenon | Describes and/or tests associations |
| Patterns or themes | Averages, frequencies |
| Non-statistical | Statistical |

# ▶ LITERATURE REVIEW

A **literature review** is a critical component of planning for evaluations, including reviewing past work and evidence, selecting strategies that have been used successfully in the past, and identifying the need and potential outcomes. A literature review provides an in-depth analysis of recently published research findings (the state of the science) in an identified area. It analyzes what is known and what is missing (gaps) in the scientific literature. Literature reviews describe the science and any existing gaps in a specifically identified area of interest. The literature review will inform the question or area of focus and guide the evaluation plan's development.

The literature review may identify evidence-based interventions that can be replicated, instruments that have been standardized and tested, procedures that can be adapted, appropriate statistical tests, and theoretical frameworks that can be used to guide the health education program or intervention and will support the evaluation plan.

Several different types of literature reviews can be conducted. It is also important to consider the scope of the review.

# ▶ SCOPE OF THE LITERATURE REVIEW

When considering how in-depth or comprehensive the review will be, consider the time period for the review. A good rule of thumb is to look for works published in the last 10 years. However, it is also important to include seminal work (e.g., studies and other work that may be older but have had a large influence on the field or topic area). Regardless, identify literature related to the problem, the planned intervention and outcomes, and strategies for evaluating how well the intervention addresses the problem.

There are many types of information you can use to inform the breadth and depth of the literature review.

**Theoretical literature** includes conceptual models, theoretical frameworks, and evidence-based plans and methodologies. This literature provides a road map for ways to think about the problem and may help the health educator identify ways of explaining behavior or the causes of the problem.

**Empirical literature** is research or past evaluation studies that tested a specific research question, including research that has tested how theories apply to behavior or observed events. This literature often describes the past literature, methods used to evaluate or test a hypothesis, the results, and discusses how the research influences health education practice or future research. Sources of literature reviews include journals, books, theses and dissertations, conference proceedings, government reports, practice guidelines, citations, and websites.

**Primary sources** are reports of original findings published in peer-reviewed journals or scholarly books. Health educators should try to use primary sources whenever possible to ensure accuracy. Examples of primary sources are clinical trials, controlled trials, studies, and dissertations and theses.

**Secondary sources** include editorials, commentaries, and articles that synthesize other studies and articles. Often, these articles summarize the findings from multiple original research studies on one health topic. Examples of secondary sources include systematic reviews, meta-analyses, qualitative synthesis, review articles, and practice guidelines.

**Systematic literature** review is a method for identifying, interpreting, and synthesizing existing research evidence.

**Meta-analyses** involve a statistical synthesis method used in some systematic reviews to quantitatively combine results from several studies and then summarize these findings.

## ▶ INTERPRETING AND REPORTING ON EVALUATION RESULTS[5,6]

After you finish with data analysis, organize and interpret the results, justify conclusions, and then communicate the findings to stakeholders and the community (Koplan et al., 1999). To justify findings from a program evaluation, health educators need to understand the limits of their data and be able to defend the merit, worth, or significance of the findings. They then need to link conclusions to the findings, based on credible evidence, and consistent with the agreed-upon values or standards of stakeholders.

Reporting and dissemination can take different forms, such as written reports, presentations, peer-reviewed manuscripts, and public forums. This step is especially important because results may affect decision-making, policy, and future programs. Recommendations from a program evaluation may influence whether a program continues, expands, is revised, or ends based on the judgments made about the program's effectiveness. Health education specialists must incorporate evidence-based practices into the design, planning, implementation, and evaluation of health education programs and interventions. Tracking and sharing lessons learned throughout the evaluation are also important. Lessons learned are also important for informed decision-making around the future of health education programs.

## ▶ DISSEMINATING FINDINGS

**Dissemination** is about making the findings from your evaluation or research available for diverse audiences through various channels or formats. For instance, you might communicate about findings through a conference, newsletter, or publication in an academic journal. Sharing data and findings with the public and those who would benefit from your health education program or intervention helps to replicate your programs and interventions in other settings and with different populations (Community Tool Box, 2021).

Your dissemination plan should consider:

1. The audience
2. Needs and interests of the audience
3. What you hope to gain from the dissemination of results
4. How you will communicate the ongoing results of your program to your audience (e.g., reports, meetings, presentations)
5. How you will communicate about the final results to any required audiences (e.g., final reports, publications, oral presentations)

---

[5] Competency 4.4 Interpret the data, copyright of the National Commission for Health Education Credentialing, Inc. (NCHEC).
[6] Competency 4.5 Use findings, copyright of the National Commission for Health Education Credentialing, Inc. (NCHEC).

# ▶ CONCLUSION

This chapter provided an overview of strategies and competencies needed to evaluate health education programs and interventions successfully. It is important to consider the type of data (quantitative and qualitative) you will collect, how you will manage and analyze the data, and how you will prepare for the reporting and dissemination of the findings. What you learned in this chapter about the evaluation is critical for ensuring the success of health education programs. In Chapter 6, you will review Area of Responsibility V: Advocacy.

1. In evaluation research, experiments with control groups:

   A. Provide the clearest evidence of a causal association
   B. Use the same intervention with both groups, to double the evidence
   C. Always place participants in groups by random assignment
   D. Are not suitable for use in public health

2. Outcomes evaluation of a program requires all of the following except:

   A. Uncertainty about the effect of the program
   B. A program with a logic model
   C. An intervention that is clearly defined
   D. A program with a theory or rationale of why it works

3. Community-based participatory research challenged all of these positive tenets except:

   A. Science is neutral and value-free
   B. There is one valid way of interpreting reality
   C. Research needs a systematic approach and clear disclosure of the methods used
   D. Because of their training, scientists are the real experts and their opinion carries more weight than that of community members

4. For the dissemination of research findings to be effective, it is necessary that:

   A. The research occurs in a neutral location
   B. They are presented once, to minimize miscommunication
   C. The intended audience can access the findings
   D. The findings are presented in a way that is convenient for the researchers

5. Which is NOT true of publishing research or program findings?

   A. May contribute to future funding
   B. Delays other research being done
   C. It is crucial to career advancement
   D. It makes it possible for other researchers to use the results

6. A local health department develops a program that includes health education and screening to reduce the number of cases of gonorrhea in the county each year. A measure of the program's outcomes would be:

   A. The number of office visits for treatment of gonorrhea
   B. The number of public service announcement (PSAs) aired on the radio
   C. The number of gonorrhea cases after the campaign
   D. The number of people who could name the signs and symptoms of gonorrhea

## 1. A) Provide the clearest evidence of a causal association

While not always feasible in evaluations, a control group provides evidence about whether a particular program caused the observed change.

## 2. B) A program with a logic model

To conduct an evaluation, you need a clearly defined intervention with a theory or rationale for why it works and the desire to understand the effect of the program. A logic model is a helpful planning and implementation tool, but it is not required, though many evaluators would develop one during the evaluation if one did not already exist.

## 3. C) Research needs a systematic approach and clear disclosure of the methods used

Regardless of the approach used, research must have a systematic approach and disclose the methods being used to conduct the research.

## 4. C) The intended audience can access the findings

For dissemination to happen effectively, the research or program findings must be distributed in places and ways that are accessible to the intended audience(s).

## 5. B) Delays other research being done

Publishing your findings does not delay future work from being conducted; it is a crucial part of your work. Whether those findings are published in the peer-reviewed literature, on your organization's website, presented at a local conference, "take-back" sessions to the community, or whatever the appropriate method of dissemination, that work is part of the research/program development process.

## 6. C) The number of gonorrhea cases after the campaign

In this case, reducing the number of people who have gonorrhea was the goal of the program, so that would be the outcome measure researched. The number of PSAs aired would be a process measure, and the number of office visits and the number of people who could name the signs/symptoms of gonorrhea would be impact, or short-term, outcomes that help you reach your long-term goal of reduction in cases.

7. Which one is NOT a common threat to internal validity?

    A. History effects
    B. Maturation effects
    C. Selection effect
    D. Hawthorne effect

8. All of the following correctly describe the characteristics of triangulations except:

    A. Triangulation means using three sets of data in studying a topic or setting
    B. Triangulation may involve contextualizing the information gathered
    C. Triangulation may involve using more than one methodological approach
    D. Triangulation is used to establish validity in qualitative research

9. An evaluator finds a statistically significant relationship between variables X and Y at the 0.05 level. What does this mean?

    A. 95 times out of 100, the results are true
    B. There is a 5% chance the results are true
    C. A person could be 90% sure that the study results were a reflection of the relationship in the population of random sampling was used
    D. If 100 samples were drawn, results like these would be obtained by chance 95% of the time

10. Which of the following is NOT true?

    A. One study, no matter how well designed or implemented, nor how large the sample, can provide definitive evidence of validity
    B. Reliability is necessary for validity to exist
    C. A measure that has been repeatedly shown to be valid for populations A and B will be valid for population C
    D. Reliability refers to how consistent the test is at returning the same result when the same results are entered

11. Which of the following is true?

    A. Reliability is a precondition to validity
    B. Validity is a precondition to reliability
    C. As validity increases, often reliability decreases
    D. While reliability addresses error, validity addresses confidence

12. The Centers for Disease Control and Prevention's (CDC) Framework for Program Evaluation's final step is:

    A. Using and sharing results
    B. Justifying conclusions
    C. Describing the program
    D. Engaging stakeholders

(See answers next page.)

## 7. D) Hawthorne effect

The Hawthorne effect is a threat to external validity. It refers to the positive reaction participants may experience just because they receive any treatment. We cannot generalize from the results if we cannot ascertain that it was explicitly and exclusively the treatment that caused the difference. Administering another treatment for the control group helps solve this problem (a placebo or standard treatment). The other answers listed are threats to internal validity.

## 8. A) Triangulation means using three sets of data in studying a topic or setting

Triangulation means exploring multiple points of view and perspectives in a given setting, establishing relationships between these perspectives, and integrating them into the analysis of findings. In a broader research context, triangulation may also involve employing multiple and differing methodological approaches and methodologies, different sources of information, and different theoretical approaches. However, these multiple, differing perspectives, approaches, and sources do not have an established number, and certainly don't have to be exactly three.

## 9. A) 95 times out of 100, the results are true

A statistically significant relationship at the level of 0.05 means that 95 times out of 100 the results truly reflect what is happening in the population. Another way of saying it is that there is a 5% chance that the results are observed due to chance alone.

## 10. C) A measure that has been repeatedly shown to be valid for populations A and B will be valid for population C

Measures can be valid, or measure what they are supposed to measure, for one (or multiple) population, but not for another. This validity is demonstrated over a series of studies.

## 11. A) Reliability is a precondition to validity

Your measure has to reliably measure what it measures before it can be valid. That is, if you get on a scale 10 times, it has to say you weigh the same each time before we can be confident it says you weigh what you actually weigh.

## 12. A) Using and sharing results

The sixth and final step is "Use and share lessons learned."

13. Which of the following is false?

    A. Reliability reduces random error
    B. Validity reduces bias
    C. Well-designed studies use measures that yield no error
    D. If researchers average random errors over many measurements, theoretically there should be zero errors as a result

14. Which section of a journal article presents the authors' steps to carry out the intervention or experiment?

    A. Overview
    B. Methods
    C. Results
    D. Discussion

15. _____ is an active, interactive, and iterative process of repetitively reading and coding transcripts until "common" insights and themes emerge.

    A. Qualitative analysis
    B. Quantitative analysis
    C. Factor analysis
    D. Power analysis

16. This process involves the random selection of cases to be representative of a population and is often used in quantitative studies.

    A. Outreach
    B. Probability sampling
    C. Non-probability sampling
    D. Convenience sampling

17. A health educator is preparing a report for a funder on an injury-reduction program in an interstate repaving work zone. He plans to report on the number of sessions he held with workers to educate them on the proper ways to wear personal protective equipment (PPE) and the topics covered in those sessions. This would be part of his:

    A. Formative evaluation
    B. Process evaluation
    C. Impact evaluation
    D. Outcome evaluation

### 13. C) Well-designed studies use measures that yield no error
No measure or technique yet invented has zero error inherent in it. We select a priori how much error we are willing to accept in our measurement and interpret our results in light of those assumptions.

### 14. B) Methods
The Methods (or Methodology) section describes the actions undertaken by the author(s) or research team to conduct the intervention or research.

### 15. A) Qualitative analysis
Qualitative analysis provides a deep, rich exploration of the data and can be assisted with software such as NVivo or Dedoose.

### 16. B) Probability sampling
Probability sampling involves the random selection (i.e., a flip of a coin) of characteristics of a population to try to mirror the priority population.

### 17. B) Process evaluation
Process evaluation determines whether program activities were implemented as they were planned.

18. A health educator is tasked with preventing death from house fires. She decides to focus on educating elementary school children and senior citizens on the risks of house fires and proper evacuation techniques, and distributes smoke detectors through the schools and at community events. If she conducted a short survey after the event at a senior center where she asked if the attendees liked the event, understood the materials she presented, and planned to install the smoke detector, that would be an example of what kind of evaluation, according to the PRECEDE-PROCEED model?

   A. Formative evaluation
   B. Process evaluation
   C. Impact evaluation
   D. Outcome evaluation

19. A health educator has been hired to develop an after-school program for a large school district in an urban/suburban area that contains a mix of both high and low-income neighborhoods. There is a small budget for a needs assessment. What would be the best method to ensure the health educator has the most representative data to plan for the needs of the families when developing his program?

   A. Nominal group process
   B. Delphi panel
   C. Focus groups
   D. Surveys

20. A logic model can help to answer the following questions except:

   A. Where is the program going?
   B. How will the program get there?
   C. Who is responsible for implementation activities?
   D. How will the program know if it has been successful?

## 18. C) Impact evaluation

According to PRECEDE-PROCEED model, immediate or short-term effects of a program are measured by impact evaluation. Some evaluation models/schools of thought view impact evaluation as looking at the final (most distal) results from an intervention.

## 19. D) Surveys

While a mixed-methods approach would probably be best, in this case, surveys would be your best answer. Neither a nominal group process nor a Delphi panel is appropriate here. Focus groups would provide interesting information, but given the disparate needs of urban/suburban populations and high/low-income families for after-school care and the small budget for needs assessment, a survey will be the best option.

## 20. C) Who is responsible for implementation activities?

Logic models answer the "big questions" about a program—where is it going, how will it get there, what will show that it has arrived. Specific details, such as who is responsible for implementing specific activities, are not generally shown on a logic model—such information is more likely found on a Gantt chart or other monitoring document.

## REFERENCES

CDC Office of Oral Health. (2017). *Step 2B: Logic models*. https://www.cdc.gov/oralhealth/state_programs/pdf/logic_models.pdf

Community Tool box. (2021). *Chapter 6: Communications to promote interest*. https://ctb.ku.edu/en/table-of-contents/participation/promoting-interest

Davis, M. V. (2006). Teaching practical public health evaluation methods. *American Journal of Evaluation, 27*(2), 247–256.

Donaldson, S. I., & Lipsey, M. W. (2006). Roles for theory in contemporary evaluation practice: Developing practical knowledge. In I. Shaw, J. Greene, & M. Mark (Eds.), *The handbook of evaluation: Policies, programs, and practices* (pp. 56–75). Sage.

Gaglio, B., Shoup, J. A., & Glasgow, R. E. (2013). The RE-AIM framework: A systematic review of use over time. *American Journal of Public Health, 103*(6), e38–e46.

Goodyear, P. (2018). Design research. *Health Education in Practice: Journal of Research for Professional Learning, 1*(1), 7–17.

Green, L. J., & Kreuter, M. W. (1999). The precede–proceed model. In L. J. Green & M. W. Kreuter (Eds.), *Health promotion planning: An educational approach* (3rd ed., pp. 32–43). Mayfield Publishing Company.

Koplan, J. P., Milstein, R. L., & Wetterhall, S. (1999). *Framework for program evaluation in public health*. U. S. Department of Health & Human Services.

Newcomer, K. E., Hatry, H. P., & Wholey, J. S. (2015). *Handbook of practical program evaluation* (4th ed.). John Wiley & Sons.

Rychetnik, L., Frommer, M., Hawe, P., & Shiell, A. (2002). Criteria for evaluating evidence on public health interventions. *Journal of Epidemiology and Community Health, 56*(2), 119–127.

Rychetnik, L., Hawe, P., Waters, E., Barratt, A., & Frommer, M. (2004). A glossary for evidence-based public health. *Journal of Epidemiology and Community Health, 58*(7), 538–545.

Saunders, R. P., Evans, M. H., & Joshi, P. (2005). Developing a process-evaluation plan for assessing health promotion program implementation: A how-to guide. *Health Promotion Practice, 6*(2), 134–147.

Scriven, M. (1998). A minimalist theory of evaluation: The least theory that practice requires. *American Journal of Evaluation, 19*, 57–70.

Thompson, N., Kegler, M., & Holtgrave, D. (2006). In R. Crosby, R. DiClemente, & L. Salazar (Eds.), *Research methods in health promotion*. Jossey-Bass.

Trochim, W. M. (2006). *The research methods knowledge base* (2nd ed.). Conjoint.ly. https://conjointly.com/kb/

# Area of Responsibility V: Advocacy[1]

## ▶ INTRODUCTION

This chapter will provide an overview of the role of health education specialists in advocacy, including identifying emerging health and policy concerns, developing coalitions, and engaging with the community. It will include a discussion of the implementation and evaluation of advocacy efforts to promote changes to health policy, system, and environments.

## ▶ ADVOCACY AND THE HEALTH EDUCATOR[2]

**Advocacy**—working to bring an issue to a decision-making level, be it within a workplace, school, local, state, or federal government level, and bring about a desired change—is an increasingly important role for health education specialists. While health educators in the past might have confined themselves mainly to education and communication, we are increasingly being called upon to serve as a resource for advocacy or engage in advocacy themselves. This section reviews two basic types of advocacy: legislative and media. The distinction between the two is not always clear-cut—the media is often used by those trying to change laws, get funding, and so on. But the division provides a helpful way to think about two different audiences (legislators and the media) and how best to interact with each. Like all communication, successful advocacy depends on a thorough understanding of your audience—what they already know, believe, and want. The major goals of advocacy are to get your audience to stay informed and take action.

Whether a health educator is lobbying to have a law or policy changed or is in the business of helping to craft policies or regulations, the steps to creating comprehensive advocacy campaigns are outlined as follows:

1. Identify current and emerging issues that may influence health and health education.
2. Access accurate resources related to identified issues.
3. Analyze the impact of existing and proposed policies on health.
4. Analyze factors that influence decision-makers and identify the significance and implication of health policy for individuals, groups, and communities.
5. Engage stakeholders in advocacy planning and activities.

---

[1] The Eight Areas of Responsibility for Health Education Specialists are copyright of the National Commission for Health Education Credentialing, Inc. (NCHEC).

[2] Competency 5.1 Identify a current or emerging health issue requiring policy, systems, or environmental change, copyright of the National Commission for Health Education Credentialing, Inc. (NCHEC).

6. Develop an advocacy plan in compliance with local, state, and/or federal laws and organizational policies and procedures.
7. Communicate the impact of health and health information on organizational and socio-ecological factors, using data where appropriate.
8. Implement advocacy plans that advocate for health-related policies, regulations, laws, or rules and use evidence-based research to develop policies to promote health, incorporating media and technology where appropriate.
9. Evaluate advocacy efforts and use evaluation and research findings in policy analysis (Figure 6.1).

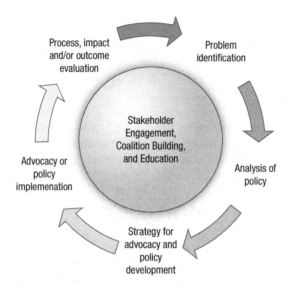

**Figure 6.1** The advocacy and policy process

*Source:* Adapted from the Centers for Disease Control and Prevention. (2015). *CDC policy process.* https://www.cdc.gov/policy/analysis/process/index.html

## LEGISLATIVE ADVOCACY

**Legislative advocacy** is, in a nutshell, contacting and working with a policymaker to discuss a public health problem and advocate for some specific solution. These could be as sweeping as raising the drinking age or banning certain types of guns, to much smaller minutia, such as adjusting reimbursement rates for a particular surgical procedure. It can also include **electioneering** or campaigning for a specific candidate for office. Depending on where you work, direct campaigning or canvassing may be prohibited during your work time or as part of your work activities; in other jobs, it may be part of your responsibilities. It is always advisable to check with your HR department to be clear about what your rights and responsibilities are as an employee in regards to advocacy.

It is critical when conducting legislative advocacy to understand your audience thoroughly. You will likely be interacting with one of two types of people: the legislator (government official) themselves or their staff members. Often, you begin interacting with a staff member and then might move on to interacting with the legislator. You might use your social media accounts to inform and reach legislators or submit an op-ed or letter to the editor of your local or regional newspapers to highlight critical public health issues and priorities in your community. The American Public Health Association (2017) offers these 10 tips for legislative advocacy:

1. Get to know legislators well—their districts and constituencies, voting records, personal schedules, opinions, expertise, and interests. Be sure to have a good understanding of the legislator and their concerns, priorities, and perspectives.
2. Acquaint yourself with the staff members for the legislators, committees, and resource officials with whom you will be working. These people are essential sources of information and have significant influence in some instances in the development of policy.
3. Identify fellow advocates and partners in the public health community to better understand the process, monitor legislation, and assess strengths and weaknesses. Finding common ground on an issue sometimes brings together strange bedfellows but makes for a stronger coalition.
4. Identify groups and other legislators with whom you may need to negotiate for changes in legislation. Do not dismiss anyone because of previous disagreements or because you lack a history of working together. "Yesterday's opponent may be today's ally."
5. Foster and strengthen relationships with allies and work with legislators who are flexible and tend to keep an open mind. Don't allow anyone to consider you a bitter enemy because you disagree.
6. Be honest, straightforward, and realistic when working with legislators and their staffs. Don't make promises you can't keep. Never lie or mislead a legislator about the importance of an issue, the opposition's position or strength, or other matters.
7. Be polite, remember names, and thank those who help you—both in the legislature and in the public health advocacy community.
8. Learn the legislative process and understand it well. Keep on top of the issues and be aware of controversial and contentious areas.
9. Be brief, clear, accurate, persuasive, timely, persistent, grateful, and polite when presenting your position and communicating what you need/want from the legislator or staff member.
10. Be sure to follow up with legislators and their staff. If you offer your assistance or promise to provide additional information, do so in a timely and professional manner. Be a reliable resource for them today and in the future.

Resources for legislative advocacy:
- American Public Health Association:
  - www.apha.org/policies-and-advocacy/advocacy-for-public-health
- Society for Public Health Educators:
  - www.sophe.org/advocacy
- National Association of County and City Health Officials:
  - www.naccho.org/advocacy

## MEDIA ADVOCACY

**Media advocacy** attempts to harness the power of the media to change or craft public perception or education around a particular topic. Media can be thought of as "free" or "paid"—free media are stories covered by the media, and paid media are advertisements that must be purchased. There are benefits to both. Obviously, with free media, there is no direct cost to the organization, but you give up control of what is covered. You control what your audience sees with paid media, but it can be expensive, and the public may perceive it as being more biased than what is covered in the free media. Which kind of media you choose, or what mix, will depend on your budget, interests, and intent. Being skilled in media advocacy means you know who to contact in the media, how to contact them, and how to deliver your message to them successfully.

Media advocacy often begins with issuing press releases, letters to the editor, policy briefs, and/or press conferences. Policy briefs often include a summary of a health problem, evidence-based best practices, relevant data, and/or policy options and recommendations to address a health problem. For an excellent resource on how to develop, craft, and evaluate these and more, read the Centers for Disease Control and Prevention's (CDC's) Healthy Communities Program *Media Access Guide: A Resource for Community Health Promotion*, available at: www.cdc.gov/nccdphp/dch/programs/healthycommunitiesprogram/tools/pdf/mediaaccessguide.pdf

Social media is another avenue for conducting media advocacy. Social media allows for both synchronous and asynchronous communications with networks, stakeholders, and lawmakers (Stellefson et al., 2020). The goal is to increase political engagement with a range of stakeholders to increase access to information, raise awareness of the need for voter registration, and voting activities and lobbying.

## COALITIONS[3]

While coalitions can be extremely helpful with planning and implementing health promotion programs, they can play an important role in advocacy. A coalition is often made up of key community stakeholders from schools, policymakers, law enforcement, and community professionals from relevant populations and community organizations with a joint interest in education and preventing the health outcomes of interest. Coalitions also can support broader leadership, participate in shared decision-making, and support communication and collaboration with communities.

Coalitions should be large enough to complete advocacy tasks but not so large that it becomes unmanageable to plan meetings and accomplish tasks. Coalitions are like other organizations or groups in that they require time, staff, and management to ensure tasks and day-to-day activities are completed. Best practices for coalition evaluation include employing a logic model, documenting community changes, and employing pre-post surveys (Kegler et al., 2020).

Resources for creating and maintaining coalitions:

- Community Tool Box:
  - https://ctb.ku.edu/en/table-of-contents/assessment/promotion-strategies/start-a-coaltion/main
  - https://ctb.ku.edu/en/creating-and-maintaining-coalitions-and-partnerships
- National Coalition Building Institute International:
  - https://ncbi.org/

*Please see* Chapter 3 *for background on community coalitions.*

## ENGAGING IN ADVOCACY EFFORTS[4]

Advocacy efforts can vary depending on the health issue, community needs, and resources to drive health policy, systems, and/or environmental change. Some potential strategies to consider include information gathering, increasing voter registration and voting activities, lobbying, grassroots lobbying, legislative advocacy, media advocacy, litigation, and additional efforts to increase community participation in advocacy and policy change (Galer-Unti, 2010).

---

[3] Competency 5.2 Engage coalitions and stakeholders in addressing the health issue and planning advocacy efforts, copyright of the National Commission for Health Education Credentialing, Inc. (NCHEC).

[4] Competency 5.3 Engage in advocacy, copyright of the National Commission for Health Education Credentialing, Inc. (NCHEC).

Examples of policy changes that health education efforts have supported include smoke-free policies, increased federal taxes on tobacco products, handgun registration and licensing laws, and increased funding for public health issues (Freudenberg, 2005).

## ADVOCACY EVALUATION[5]

As with any other intervention, evaluation is critical, but is often overlooked in advocacy. To assess the results of advocacy work, a health education specialist must have gone into the advocacy work with clear goals and SMART (specific, measurable, attainable, realistic, and time-sensitive) objectives in mind. Thoughtful development of such goals and objectives will pave the way for an effective evaluation. For instance, a process evaluation might focus on how the program staff implemented the advocacy efforts and identified differences between the planned and actual implementation. For an impact or outcome evaluation, health educators might examine how key indicators changed after the advocacy efforts.

Creating a logic model will help to visualize the key aspects of your advocacy efforts systematically. List the inputs, activities, outputs, and your potential short-term, intermediate, and long-term impacts. You will also need to identify a data collection plan, such as using existing data and other outcomes related to the advocacy efforts.

See the following resources from the CDC:

- www.cdc.gov/eval/
- www.cdc.gov/policy/analysis/process/index.html
- www.cdc.gov/injury/pdfs/policy/brief%201-a.pdf
- https://www.cdc.gov/injury/pdfs/policy/Appendices-a.pdf

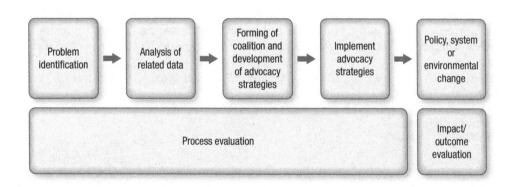

**Figure 6.2** Diagram for advocacy evaluation

Common evaluation questions related to policy and advocacy include:
Process:

- Number of communications issued (press releases, blog posts, letters to the editor, etc.)
- Number of meetings held with the community
- Web/social media traffic on the issue

---

[5] Competency 5.4 Evaluation advocacy, copyright of the National Commission for Health Education Credentialing, Inc. (NCHEC).

- Number of meetings held with elected officials
- Number of letters/calls to elected officials in support of the organization's position

Impact/Outcome:

- Was public awareness of the problem raised?
- Was public support for the desired change increased?
- Were additional people/organizations recruited to the organization/coalition?
- Did the organization gain funding?
- Did policymakers' support increase?
- Was there movement through the legislative process?
- Were policies implemented (or, conversely, blocked or removed)?

Finally, it will also be essential to consider how you will share the evaluation findings—planning for how to report and disseminate the evaluation findings is also a key step in the evaluation process. You will need to identify your target audience, format and focus of the communications, ways to best frame messaging, methods for delivering your messages, and the potential need for developing communication materials.

# ▶ CONCLUSION

This chapter highlights the role that health education specialists can play in advocating for changes to health issues that require policy, system, and/or environmental change. There are several tools at your fingertips to increase awareness and advocate for policy change that will improve public health and the lives of community members. These may include coalition-building activities, legislative advocacy, media advocacy, and grassroots lobbying. Much like health education programs, it is crucial to evaluate advocacy activities' process, impact, and outcomes. Finally, you should consider disseminating evaluation results to the stakeholders and community members involved and/or impacted by the advocacy and policy change.

*For more details on evaluation, please see* Chapter 5 *for evaluation strategies and* Chapter 7 *on health communications.*

1. A group of health educators wants to meet with a senator to advocate for a cap on prescription drug prices. Which is NOT a best practice for face-to-face meetings with policymakers?

    A. Be brief and stick to the topic at hand
    B. Select several people to present data at the meeting
    C. Make an appointment
    D. Leave written materials (e.g., fact sheets) with the senator/staff

2. The average age of representatives/senators in the 117th Congress was:

    A. 51/56 years old
    B. 58/64 years old
    C. 61/54 years old
    D. 72/78 years old

3. Which of the following is the correct order for developing an advocacy campaign?

    A. Identify the health issues>Analyze current policy and influencing factors>Engage stakeholders>Develop advocacy plan
    B. Engage stakeholders> Identify health issues>Analyze current policy and influencing factors>Develop advocacy plan
    C. Engage stakeholders>Identify health issues>Create communication materials>Develop advocacy plan
    D. Identify the health issues>Engage stakeholders>Analyze current policy and influencing factors>Develop advocacy plan

4. A health educator is applying the Transtheoretical Model to characterize how much change there has been in various policymakers' intentions to support a price cap on prescription drugs after their coalition met with various members of the legislative body. The health educator is doing:

    A. Research
    B. Program evaluation
    C. Advocacy planning
    D. Advocacy evaluation

5. Suppose a particular legislator had not previously supported the need to increase the number of conditions screened for in her state's Newborn Screening Program but is now introducing a bill to require such an increase. How would you characterize her stages of change?

    A. Moved from precontemplation to contemplation
    B. Moved from contemplation to preparation
    C. Moved from precontemplation to action
    D. Moved from contemplation to action

## 1. B) Select several people to present data at the meeting
It is best practice to appoint one spokesperson for a meeting with a policymaker.

## 2. B) 58/64 years old
The average age of members of the House at the beginning of the 117th Congress was 58.4 years and for senators, 64.3 years.

## 3. A) Identify the health issues>Analyze current policy and influencing factors>Engage stakeholders>Develop advocacy plan
The first step is to identify the health issues. The next steps are to analyze resources, the impact of existing/proposed policies on health, and factors that influence decision-makers. Next, you engage stakeholders and finally develop your plan.

## 4. D) Advocacy evaluation
The health educator is evaluating their advocacy efforts using the Transtheoretical Model.

## 5. C) Moved from Precontemplation to Action
The legislator moved from not believing something needed to be changed (precontemplation) to taking action to change the number of screenings required.

6. _____ is when individuals or organizations work together to build coalitions, influence public opinion, create an agenda, and/or communicate through the media about a specific topic or topics.

   A. Advocacy
   B. Advising
   C. Activism
   D. Agenda-setting

7. A key distinction between advocacy and lobbying is:

   A. Lobbying is unethical
   B. Lobbying includes requesting action on a specific piece of legislation
   C. Advocacy is done at the grassroots level, and lobbying is done directly
   D. There is no difference

8. Which of the following is NOT considered a step to creating a comprehensive advocacy campaign?

   A. Analyze the impact of existing and proposed policies on health
   B. Engage stakeholders in advocacy planning and activities
   C. Develop evaluation as a part of the planning
   D. Develop durable messages that can be used for future campaigns

9. Legislative advocacy is considered to involve:

   A. Contacting and working with a policymaker to discuss a public health problem
   B. Developing health education marketing materials
   C. Sharing program implementation outcomes with stakeholders
   D. Developing agendas and planning meetings

10. _____ is a bill or resolution that has been passed by both chambers of the U.S. Congress and signed into law by the president.

   A. Advocacy
   B. Act
   C. Legislator
   D. Amendment

11. Which of the following is considered to occur when individuals, coalitions, or organizations use media to advance a health initiative?

   A. Media relations
   B. Policymaker
   C. Media advocacy
   D. Legislation

## 6. A) Advocacy
Advocacy work ultimately desires to change something through influencing opinion via the media, public opinion, or directly to policymakers.

## 7. B) Lobbying includes requesting action on a specific piece of legislation
While both advocacy and lobbying consist of communication with government officials with a clear agenda, the Centers for Disease Control and Prevention (CDC) differentiates lobbying as also referring to specific legislation or other executive order, reflects a point of view, and contains an overt call to action.

## 8. D) Develop durable messages that can be used for future campaigns
The steps to creating comprehensive advocacy campaigns include both analyzing existing and proposed laws and policies as well as engaging stakeholders in planning activities to support these existing and newly proposed laws or policies and considering evaluation. Messages should be specific to the campaign, as the advocacy landscape is constantly changing.

## 9. A) Contacting and working with a policymaker to discuss a public health problem
Legislative advocacy is, in a nutshell, contacting and working with a policymaker to discuss a public health problem and advocate for some specific solution. These could be as sweeping as raising the drinking age or banning certain types of guns, to much smaller minutia, such as adjusting reimbursement rates for a particular kind of surgical procedure.

## 10. B) Act
An act is a bill or resolution that has been passed by both chambers of the U.S. Congress and signed into law by the president.

## 11. C) Media advocacy
Media advocacy is when mass media is used to influence or advance public policy.

12. A health educator has identified an emerging issue that is affecting the health of people in her community. She believes she needs to engage in advocacy with state lawmakers to change a policy that is exacerbating the health condition. What would be her next step?

   A. Gather information about the health topic from reliable resources
   B. Set goals and objectives
   C. Join a coalition of organizations and people interested in the health topic
   D. Draft a letter to state lawmakers

13. _____ involves adding value judgment about the need for policy change and educating policymakers about an issue.

   A. Decision-making
   B. Health education
   C. Lobbying
   D. Advocacy

14. Health policy advocacy can affect and help sustain population-level health behavior change by:

   A. Changing the surrounding environment
   B. Conducting research
   C. Educating individuals
   D. Changing knowledge

15. Advocacy is different from lobbying in which of the following ways?

   A. It involves asking policymakers to change laws
   B. It involves creating awareness of the need for policy change
   C. It involves asking policymakers to dismiss a policy or piece of legislation
   D. It involves an attempt to influence specific legislation

16. Which of the following is NOT directly involved in organizing, financing, and implementing health-related policy?

   A. The media
   B. Congress
   C. Healthcare providers
   D. Local communities

17. A health educator has determined, through reviewing the literature, holding several focus groups, and collecting surveys from the population of interest, that lobbying is necessary to create a new law that will protect the public's health. What should the next step be?

   A. Begin planning an advocacy campaign
   B. Hold public meetings to rally support for changing the law
   C. Check their workplace's policy on advocacy activities
   D. Hold a press conference

## 12. A) Gather information about the health topic from reliable resources

After identifying a health topic, the second step in engaging the advocacy process is to gather information about the health topic from reliable resources. These can include peer-reviewed journals, federal or state repositories of vital statistics, reputable nongovernmental organization (NGO) sources, or primary data.

## 13. C) Lobbying

Advocacy involves adding value judgment about the need for policy change and educating policymakers about issue.

## 14. A) Changing the surrounding environment

Health policy advocacy can affect and help sustain population-level health behavior change by changing the surrounding environment. This might include changing the availability of sidewalks, addressing crime, or increasing green spaces to promote recreational activities.

## 15. B) It involves creating awareness of the need for policy change

Advocacy primarily involves educating and mobilizing communities to be aware of the need for policy or legislation change. Lobbying involves more direct efforts to change, dismiss, or influence a policy or legislation.

## 16. A) The media

The media may be a conduit through which policies are advocated for and communicated through, but they do not directly affect the creation and delivery of health policy.

## 17. C) Check their workplace's policy on advocacy activities

Federal, state, and organizational laws and policies may prohibit lobbying by organizations. A health educator should know the rules for lobbying before embarking on a lobbying campaign.

18. _____ allows for both synchronous and asynchronous communications with networks, stakeholders, and law makers.

   A. Policy briefs
   B. Social media
   C. Fact sheets
   D. Direct lobbying

19. Evaluation of advocacy efforts generally includes all of the following except:

   A. How the advocacy efforts were implemented
   B. Changes to key health indicators after advocacy efforts and policy change
   C. Program staff turnover
   D. How much money was spent on the campaign

20. A process evaluation of advocacy efforts might answer which of the following questions?

   A. Was public awareness of the problem raised?
   B. Was public support for the desired change increased?
   C. How many meetings were held with elected officials?
   D. Was a law changed?

### 18. B) Social media

Social media allows for both synchronous and asynchronous communications with networks, stakeholders, and lawmakers.

### 19. C) Program staff turnover

Evaluation might focus on how the advocacy efforts were implemented; what the identifying differences were between the planned and actual implementation; and which key indicators may have changed after the advocacy efforts were completed. Employment issues are generally an issue for human resources (HR).

### 20. D) Was a law changed?

Process evaluations determine whether program activities have been implemented as intended. Tracking how many program activities occurred are typical process measures.

# REFERENCES

American Public Health Association. (2017). *The power of advocacy.* https://www.apha.org/-/media/Files/PDF/advocacy/Power_of_Advocacy.ashx

Centers for Disease Control and Prevention. (2015). *CDC policy process.* https://www.cdc.gov/policy/analysis/process/index.html

Freudenberg, N. (2005). Public health advocacy to change corporate practices: Implications for health education practice and research. *Health Education & Behavior, 32*(3), 298–319. https://doi.org/10.1177/1090198105275044

Galer-Unti, R. A. (2010). Advocacy 2.0: Advocating in the digital age. *Health Promotion Practice, 11*(6), 784–787. https://doi.org/10.1177/1524839910386952

Kegler, M. C., Halpin, S. N., & Butterfoss, F. D. (2020). Evaluation methods commonly used to assess effectiveness of community coalitions in public health: Results from a scoping review. *Evaluating Community Coalitions and Collaboratives, 165,* 139–157.

Stellefson, M., Paige, S. R., Chaney, B. H., & Chaney, J. D. (2020). Evolving role of social media in health promotion: Updated responsibilities for health education specialists. *International Journal of Environmental Research and Public Health, 17*(4), 1153. https://doi.org/10.3390/ijerph17041153

# Area of Responsibility VI: Communications[1]

## ▶ INTRODUCTION

This chapter covers health communication. In some ways, it reviews Chapters 2 to 5 in that it is structured to begin with assessing communication needs and carries on through the process through planning, implementation, and evaluation. The HESPA II 2020 model is a major change from the way National Commission for Health Education Credentialing, Inc. (NCHEC) had earlier approached communication, when it was combined with Advocacy (now Area V). In our opinion, this is an important change because both advocacy and communication are substantial areas of work for health educators and both deserve their own area to fully explore the breadth of information they cover.

A health education specialist who practices in a community setting for a disease-specific organization—say, heart disease—will have to be able to develop program materials across a wide range of channels (e.g., pamphlets, websites, social media, and face-to-face at community health fairs). He or she may also have to write letters to the editor, issue press releases, and be available as a resource to the media when stories about heart disease or the organization arise. Additionally, they may be asked to provide resources to patients, clinicians, or other organizations to help lobby for funding, resolutions, or legislation.

A health education specialist in a collegiate setting might be tasked with developing a tobacco-free campus. They would first have to assess the communication needs of the campus and set goals and objectives for the campaign. They would also have to educate faculty, staff, and students about the need for such a change and the dangers of smoking and secondhand smoke. The health education specialist would then need to engage with smokers to answer their questions and make sure they understood the upcoming changes and how to access available smoking cessation programs. Appropriate signage, educational materials, and intranet/internet messaging would need to be developed. The health education specialist would likely work with the media to promote the college's decision throughout the community, and might try to advocate for local laws to be changed to reduce smoking or for additional funding for smoking cessation and prevention programs.

In other settings—school (K–12), healthcare, workplace, and so on—the roles and responsibilities around communication are similar. Health communication is an area where all your skills as a health educator come together to move programs, funding, and education forward within your chosen setting.[2]

---

[1] The Eight Areas of Responsibility for Health Education Specialists are copyright of the National Commission for Health Education Credentialing, Inc. (NCHEC).

[2] Competency 6.1 Determine factors that affect communication with the identified audiences, copyright of the National Commission for Health Education Credentialing, Inc. (NCHEC).

# ▶ ASSESS NEEDS FOR INFORMATION[3]

By now, it will come as no surprise that we begin the process of providing education by assessing needs. Sometimes these needs will be obvious (e.g., you are asked by your boss to provide a training in health literacy to nurses who work in your unit), and sometimes it will be your job to assess what the needs are in your work setting (e.g., you oversee workforce development or are a training director). Remember, from Chapter 2, the steps of a needs assessment:

1. Determine the purpose of the needs assessment.
2. Identify available data to assess the problem.
3. Decide on data collection approach and gather data.
4. Analyze and interpret the data.
5. Identify factors linked to the problem (in this case, the lack of sufficient knowledge).
6. Identify the focus of the training and begin the planning process.

In this, as in all needs assessments, you must always be mindful of what your available resources are. Resources are largely composed of time, money, and staff. While the earlier steps seem formal, they can be done with varying levels of resources.

Next, you have to gather your data to support your assessment of your training needs. As discussed in Chapter 2, there are a lot of ways to gather this data, both qualitatively and quantitatively. Your worksite, for example, might have a health risk assessment that gives you some insight that perhaps your employees need some education about what are low-risk levels of alcohol use. Or, reviewing your home visiting nurses' notes might reveal that they are spending a lot of time helping their clients prepare healthy meals but are frustrated by a lack of recipes that are inexpensive and easy to make. Those are both examples of using primary data—data you have collected and analyzed. You might instead be looking at secondary data—data that someone else have collected and analyzed. An example of using secondary data might be if you were working as a health educator in the county health department and you reviewed the Centers for Disease Control and Prevention's (CDC) Behavioral Risk Factor Surveillance System and discovered that your community has particularly high levels of skin cancer.

Not all health needs can be fully addressed through the delivery of information. In this section, however, we are focusing on issues that can—at least partly—be addressed by education. Depending on what your needs assessment finds, make note of issues that may not be fully addressed by education alone, and revisit them later to identify what other interventions might be needed.

Hopefully, at this point you are left with an idea of what your audience's needs are for information. You can then move into the next stage, which is planning your educational or training intervention.

# ▶ IDENTIFY VALID INFORMATION RESOURCES

When it comes to obtaining health information, to paraphrase Charles Dickens, now truly is the best of times AND the worst of times. Never in human history has there been such unfettered access to such large amounts of information. At any time of the day or night, from anywhere that has access to an internet connection (at least in countries that allow unfettered

---

[3] Competency 6.2 Determine communication objective(s) for audience(s), copyright of the National Commission for Health Education Credentialing, Inc. (NCHEC).

internet access!), you can find just about any kind of information, opinion, data, or question on nearly any topic imaginable (though the internet still cannot tell me where I left my glasses, unfortunately.) On the upside, health educators in the 21st century have close to the sum of human knowledge at their fingertips: We can look up the correct dosing for a 2-year-old's ibuprofen, the number of calories in a medium-sized apple, or the best practices for smoking cessation. On the downside, however, there is also a lot of misleading, outdated, biased, and just plain wrong information out there as well—not just on the internet but also in books, TV shows, radio, and from your friends and family (sorry, Mom). The sheer volume of information available itself can be overwhelming, so how do we find good sources of accurate information quickly? This is a critical skill for health educators to develop. In modern times, it seems less important to know some particular fact or piece of information than to know where to get a particular fact or piece of information.

Separating good information from bad and finding what information you need out of all the information available will be necessary for your professional development. While it is impossible to list all of the sources of good information or to guarantee that everything you find, even from reliable sources, is true, useful, and up to date, there are some basic guidelines to help you narrow your search and think critically about what you find.

Books, pamphlets, journal articles, and professional presentations are just some of the many sources of information you may be asked to review. In general, items that have been peer reviewed (such as articles from juried scientific journals) or are from governmental sources are considered more likely to be accurate and free from bias, but even then we should not rely on only one source of information—many times, studies published in peer-reviewed literature have later been disproven or disputed. Major professional associations such as the American Medical Association, American Academy of Pediatrics, American Public Health Association, Society of Public Health Educators, and others are also considered legitimate sources of information, though the same caveats apply. Books are harder to judge and require knowing whether the author is legitimate or not. Credentials can help you determine that, as well as if the book has been reviewed by others you know to be credible (many peer-reviewed journals do book reviews). A librarian can help you judge whether the information in a book fits what you are looking for. As always, if you are seeing similar information from a variety of sources, you can feel more confident it is good information.

## ▶ LANGUAGES SPOKEN IN THE UNITED STATES

According to Hernandez, Dietrich, & Bauman (2022), over 238 million Americans (about 78%) speak English at home. The 10 most commonly spoken languages at home (other than English) in the United States are:

1. Spanish—40,709,597
2. Chinese—3,414,146
3. French—2,060,721
4. Tagalog—1,727,002
5. Vietnamese—1,507,354
6. Arabic—1,200,927
7. Korean—1,085,735
8. Russian—920,018
9. German—903,880
10. Hindi—850,975

## HEALTH LITERACY

Perhaps the most critical element to consider when preparing your information for dissemination is the health literacy level of your audience. While often conceived of as an individual-level determinate, Healthy People 2030 recently expanded its definition of health literacy to include organizations as well. The new definitions read:

**Personal health literacy** is the degree to which individuals have the ability to find, understand, and use information and services to inform health-related decisions and actions for themselves and others.

**Organizational health literacy** is the degree to which organizations equitably enable individuals to find, understand, and use information and services to inform health-related decisions and actions for themselves and others (Office of Disease Prevention and Health Promotion, n.d.).

Health literacy affects a person's ability to:

- Navigate the healthcare system, including filling out complex forms and locating providers and services.
- Share personal information, such as health history, with providers.
- Engage in self-care and chronic disease management.
- Understand mathematical concepts such as probability and risk.

## WHY IS HEALTH LITERACY IMPORTANT?

While it may seem shocking, according to the National Assessment of Adult Literacy only 12% of U.S. adults have "proficient" levels of health literacy. Fourteen percent of adults (30 million people) have below basic health literacy, and an additional 22% have "basic" levels of health literacy—a combined 36% of the adult population in the United States with insufficient levels of health literacy to be able to fully manage their health. These adults were more likely to report their health as poor (42%) and are more likely to lack health insurance (28%) than adults with proficient health literacy. Indeed, poor health literacy is a better predictor of low health status than age, race, education level, or income (National Center for Education Statistics, 2006).

## WHO IS AT RISK?

Populations most likely to experience low health literacy are:

- Older adults
- Racial and ethnic minorities
- People with less than a high school degree or General Educational Development (GED) certificate
- People with low-income levels
- Nonnative English speakers
- People with compromised health status

## WHAT COMPRISES HEALTH LITERACY?

- Prose literacy (the ability to read)
- Numeracy

- Ability to navigate the healthcare system as well as other civic systems (e.g., transportation)
- Cultural competency

## WHAT IS NUMERACY?

Health literacy includes numeracy skills, which you can think of as being literacy for numbers and basic math. Just like literacy, people can have high, medium, or low levels.

Low numeracy can affect health because it can make it hard to:

- Understand and manage cholesterol and blood sugar levels.
- Correctly dose medication—for example, knowing the difference between "1 T" and "1 t" of liquid medicine, or finding the appropriate dose based on weight.
- Read nutrition labels, which require people to understand different measurements (e.g., mg, kcals, mcgs) as well as percentages, addition, and so on.
- Buy and use health insurance, which requires the ability to compare different plan prices, co-pays, deductibles, and so on.
- Understand a story in the newspaper about health if it involves reading bar charts, pie charts, and so on.

Here are some tips for producing readable materials:

- Write using plain language. Plain language—or "living room language"—is communication that users can understand the first time they read or hear it.
- Organize your information so that the most important points come first. People with low literacy levels take a longer time to read and may give up partway through a piece. By putting the most important information first, there is a better chance it will be read.
- Break complex information into understandable chunks. Chunking is a valuable tool for helping people understand and retain information. It is why we write phone numbers this way—(888) 555-1212—instead of this way—8885551212. Which would you rather see?
- Use formatting (headers, bold, underline, colors, boxes, etc.) to help the reader navigate your text. Bullets and numbered lists can help break up long sentences and make lists much easier to understand.
- Use simple language and define technical terms. What are the most important things to do or know?
- Assume people may have trouble with numbers. Many people, even those with higher levels of education, struggle with math and quantitative concepts—particularly statistics. Use only those that are really necessary and consider using visuals as well as words to convey the information. Sports and gambling analogies are "everyday" language and concepts that may help people understand what you are saying if you have to talk about odds or very small or very large numbers. For example, framing a risk of 1 in 75,000 in terms of "one person at a sold-out game at the Superdome gets sick" might help the audience understand that likelihood, especially if accompanied by a visual of a sold-out game at the Superdome.
- Use the active voice. The structure for active voice is generally "subject-verb-object." For example, "Mary threw the ball at the dog." Passive voice, on the other hand, obscures the actor by omitting them: "The ball was thrown at the dog." If you can add the phrase "by zombies" at the end of your sentence ("The ball was thrown at the dog by zombies"), your sentence uses passive voice. Another way to look at it is if you have a form of the

verb "to be" and a past participle, it is likely passive voice. Active voice is much easier to understand, making it a better choice for clear communication.

■ Use commonly available readability programs to check your work. Word processing programs normally have a readability checker, and it is a good idea to use it consistently to check reading level. If you do not use a program for word processing with a reading-level checker, many free websites allow you to import or copy and paste your text into the website to get the reading level of the text. Each population is different, but for a general audience, aim for sixth- to eighth-grade reading level.

■ Test your materials with the members of your audience. Words or concepts that sound easy to you may not be so to a less literate population.

## TEACH-BACK METHOD

One commonly used tool to assess how well information has been understood by an audience is the "teach-back method" (Agency for Healthcare Research and Quality [AHRQ], 2020). This method is usually used in face-to-face educational settings. The teacher will teach the information to the student and then ask the student to teach the information back to the teacher. Teach-back is a powerful tool because it simulates a time when learners are on their own trying to use the information or skills they have been given or are even teaching someone else about what they have been taught. If you are teaching complex information or skills that need multiple steps, you can "chunk and check" at points along the way—that is, do teach-back at different points during the lesson to make sure the student has mastered all the necessary information.

The conversation might go something like this:

*Teacher:* Now that I have explained to you how to cook chicken, please show me how you are going to test it at home to make sure it is done.

Student: I am going to take the meat thermometer and put it all the way into the chicken breast, but make sure I do not hit the bone.

*Teacher:* And how will you know it is done?

Student: When it is 165 degrees.

*Teacher:* So, is this one done?

Student (reading thermometer): 167, so, yes, it is done.

*Teacher:* That is right—you are ready to go!

Sometimes in using teach-back you discover that there are misunderstandings or pieces of information your students did not learn. Teach-back is a great way to uncover those misunderstandings and be able to correct them. Reimagine the previous scenario, but this time it does not go so smoothly:

*Teacher:* Now that I have explained to you how to cook chicken, please show me how you are going to test it at home to make sure it is done.

Student: I am going to take the meat thermometer and put it all the way into the chicken breast.

*Teacher:* Now, we talked about where in the meat to measure the temperature—is that thermometer in the right place?

Student: Oops, no, it is touching the bone [Backs it out a little].

*Teacher:* And how will you know it is done?

Student: When it is 145 degrees.

*Teacher:* I know that is what a lot of people think is safe for chicken breasts, but the U.S. Department of Agriculture (USDA) recommends 165 degrees for chicken breasts, too.

Student: This one is only 150 degrees.

*Teacher:* So, what are you going to do?

Student: Put it back in the oven for a few minutes and recheck it.

(A few minutes later.)

Student: Is this the right place to check the temperature?

*Teacher:* Looks great! What does the thermometer say?

Student (reading thermometer): 167, so, yes, it is done.

*Teacher:* That is right—you are ready to go!

## ▶ CHANNEL SELECTION

Channel selection is a crucial decision in communication planning. Selecting the right channels to relay your message starts with identifying the times, places, and states of mind in which your audience is receptive to and able to act upon the information or messages you wish to relay to them. Select channels that will reach your intended audiences and deliver the messages to them in a way they understand, want, retain, and can act upon. Think about the lessons discussed in the health literacy section: If people have low levels of literacy, for example, then print channels are best avoided. Audiences who are functionally literate but have low levels of science literacy or numeracy may do best with channels that allow for substantial visual supports, such as video, or interpersonal channels that allow for the assessment of learning, such as teach-back. Obviously, cost is another factor that health educators have to consider. Perhaps television advertising would be your first choice because it would reach a lot of people and you could target your audience through placing advertisements on particular shows and times, but the costs of producing and placing those ads are out of your budget . Picking the right mix of channels to go with your messages, audiences, staff time, abilities, and budgets is always a challenge for even the most experienced health educators. Rarely is one channel sufficient to successfully address health education needs. A health educator working at a student health center on stress reduction around finals time might put up posters, use digital media boards, hold stress-reduction classes, bring in therapy dogs, and utilize social media to get stress-reduction messages to students. A community health educator trying to get parents in a community with high asthma rates to make and keep follow-up appointments with their child's specialist care providers may produce pamphlets, make reminder phone calls, send text messages, design bus ads, or work with religious leaders to get the message out that follow-up care is important. For a more in-depth look at new media, including types, who uses each type of media, and their relative strengths and weaknesses, please see the New Media and Other Innovative Tools section in this chapter.

## SETTING GOALS AND OBJECTIVES[4]

### Tailored or Targeted Messages[5] (Develop message(s) using communication theories and models)

According to Hawkins et al. (2008), **tailoring** refers to creating materials customized to a specific individual, whereas **targeting** refers to creating materials customized to a specific set of audience criteria. Messages can be tailored or targeted to a number of factors, such as demographics, stage of change, knowledge, attitude, or health literacy level. Tailored health messages require knowledge of an individual's characteristics and will be specific to that individual. Tailoring and targeting materials can increase their effectiveness, though research is continuing to explore the best ways to do so.

### Tailor Messages to Distinct Subgroups

Audience segmentation is an important technique for making sure that messages and interventions meet the unique and possibly contradictory needs of different audiences. By segmenting, or tailoring, messages to distinct subgroups, health educators can address the specific needs, beliefs, and behaviors of each group. At first blush, many health educators consider demographics such as age, race, or sex as characteristics on which to tailor materials. However, there are often considerably more effective characteristics to consider. Consider the stage of change (see Chapter 9) your participants are in—those in precontemplation (those not considering change) may need awareness-raising messages to get them thinking about why a change might be necessary, while those already in action may need supportive or reinforcement messages. Knowing what stage your population has reached is critical for ensuring the right messages get to the right people.

Similarly, sometimes messages are segmented in a doer/nondoer dichotomy. People eating five servings a day of fruits and vegetables may need reinforcement for doing so in order to stave off boredom, or they might be willing to spread the message to their friends and family. Those who are not eating much in the way of fruits and vegetables may need encouragement to add, say, one serving a day. Both groups might be interested in recipes, coupons, or tips, but how those tools are presented may need to be different. Similarly, messages on sex, pregnancy, and child care are more likely to be effective if they are tailored to novices or to those with considerable experience. A third-time mother likely is looking for very different information (reminders or recommendations that have changed since her last pregnancy) in very different formats (quick and easy) than a first-time mother, to whom everything is new.

There are as many segmentation strategies as there are audiences. Knowing to whom you are speaking and what their needs/concerns are will help you identify the correct behavior-change strategy.

## HEALTH COMMUNICATION THEORIES[6]

Beyond behavioral or organizational change theories, the following theories and models help explain how communication works (or does not). When creating health communication

---

[4] Competency 6.3 Determine communication objective(s) for audiences, copyright of the National Commission for Health Education Credentialing, Inc. (NCHEC).

[5] Competency 6.4 Select methods and technologies used to deliver message(s), copyright of the National Commission for Health Education Credentialing, Inc. (NCHEC).

[6] Competency 6.5 Develop messages using communication theories and/or models, copyright of the National Commission for Health Education Credentialing, Inc. (NCHEC).

messages, materials, and campaigns, you should consider not only what behavioral theories are relevant to your work, but what theories of communication will best underpin your activities.

## Communication for Persuasion

McGuire's Persuasive Communication strategy describes the components of successful communication:

1. Credible message source (*sender*)
2. Intended audience (*receiver*)
3. Delivery *channel*
4. Message design
5. Intended behavioral *response*

McGuire also described 12 steps through which a message must go to create behavior change. These steps also give evaluators an opportunity to see where a message may have failed, for each step is linear and progressive. The 12 steps are:

1. Exposure to the message
2. Attention to the message
3. Interest in/personal relevance seen in the message
4. Understanding the message
5. Ability to adapt the message to one's own situation
6. Believing the message
7. Remembering the message in the appropriate context
8. Being able to do the behavior in the message
9. Making the decision to actually do the behavior when one thinks of it
10. Making the behavior change
11. Being reinforced for the behavior
12. Maintaining the behavior

### Further Reading

McGuire, W. J. (1984). Public communication as a strategy for inducing health-promoting behavioral change. *Preventive Medicine, 13*(3), 299–313. doi:1 0.1016/0091-7435(84)90086-0

## Elaboration Likelihood Model

The Elaboration Likelihood Model (ELM) posits that if people are engaged or interested in a particular behavior, then they will pay more attention to (elaborate on) new information presented to them about the behavior. If people are not already engaged on an issue, they will require additional stimuli (e.g., peripheral cues such as a spokesperson, models, colors, or music) to be persuaded. Beliefs and behaviors developed under the peripheral processing route are less durable than those developed under the central processing route, and therefore require frequent reinforcement.

Advertisers often use this model to design messages. An advertisement for a product that people care less about—say, toothpaste—will likely use lots of peripheral cues—an attractive model, cute slogans, catchy jingles—to help persuade the viewer that Brand A of toothpaste is the one to buy. Something in which the viewer is more interested, however—such as information on a disease that the person has recently been diagnosed with—will be more centrally processed and judged on the merits of the message, not on the message heuristics.

*Further Reading*

Petty, R., & Cacioppo, J. (1986). *Communication and persuasion: Central and peripheral routes to attitude change.* Springer-Verlag.

## EXTENDED PARALLEL PROCESSING MODEL

The Extended Parallel Processing Model (EPPM) helps understand how fear of a particular outcome may influence a person's decision-making process. The EPPM has four constructs to predict the likely outcome of communications that use a fear appeal:

- **Self-efficacy**—The extent to which a person believes that they are able to control the risk.
- **Response efficacy**—The extent to which a person believes that the suggested action, if carried out, will successfully control the risk.
- **Susceptibility**—The perception the person has of how likely the threat will affect them.
- **Severity**—The perception the person has of how serious the threat is.

Based on these four constructs, the theory predicts one of three possible outcomes to communication materials:

1. **Danger control**—When a person perceives that the severity and susceptibility are high and also perceives that they are competent to make changes, then they are likely to act to control the danger.
2. **Fear control**—The model predicts that if a person perceives their ability to control a risk as low, even if the severity and susceptibility is perceived as high, then they are likely to take steps to control their fear instead. This is undesirable because it does not lead to the desired behavior change; rather, it may lead to denial or fatalism. Many people consider it unethical to use fear-based messages in this situation because they may cause more harm than good. Steps must first be taken to raise an individual's self-efficacy before fear messages may safely and effectively be used.
3. **No response**—The severity or susceptibility of the danger was perceived as low; therefore, the person made no changes.

*Further Reading*

Witte, K. (1994). Fear control and danger control: A test of the extended parallel process model. *Communication Monographs, 61*(2), 113–134. doi:10.1080/036377 59409376328

Gore, T. D., Bracken, C. C. (2005). Testing the theoretical design of a health risk message: Reexaming the major tenants of the extended parallel process model. *Health Education and Behavior, 32*(1) 27-41. doi: 10.1177/1090198104266901. PMID: 15642752.

## *Educational Entertainment*

Educational Entertainment ("edutainment") is the intentional use of educational material in entertainment material. With roots in traditional oral and performance arts, edutainment became more formalized with the age of television, appearing as early as the 1950s but more widely in the 1960s and 1970s, particularly with the advent of telenovela. Edutainment has its roots in a variety of behavioral change and narrative theories such as the Social Cognitive

Model and Narrative Transportation. In the last two decades, it has been most often used to educate or promote behavior change at the individual level, with HIV being the single most commonly explored topic globally. Behavior change is thought to be brought about by (a) promoting behavioral and social norms, and by (b) narrative transportation, which is the degree to which the audience is so engaged they become wholly involved in the story. We can all probably remember times when we have been so swept away in a TV show, book, or movie that we almost forget that it is a story, and not real. It has been shown to be an effective method of reducing stigma and encouraging testing, but also has the potential to promote negative behaviors, such as eating disorders and suicide.

### Further Reading

Sood, S., Riley, A. H., & Alarcon, K. (2017). Entertainment-education and health and risk messaging. In R. Parrott (Ed.), *Oxford research encyclopedia of communication* (pp. 1–51). Oxford University Press.

## ▶ SOCIAL MARKETING

Social marketing is a powerful but often misunderstood tool. Social marketing, as described by Lefebvre and Flora (1988), is the "design, implementation, and control of programs aimed at increasing the acceptability of a social idea, practice [or product] in one or more groups of target adopters. The process actively involves the target population, who voluntarily exchange their time and attention for help in meeting their health needs as they perceive them."

Social marketing borrows heavily from commercial marketing techniques, but aims to sell a healthy behavior rather than, say, toothpaste. Perhaps the most well-known concept from social marketing is that of the "four Ps": product, price, place, and promotion. Each concept is discussed in the following section with an example from the CDC's VERB campaign (CDC, 2010), a nationwide, multicultural social marketing campaign conducted between 2002 and 2006 and aimed at encouraging youth ages 9 to 13 to engage in physical activity daily.

- Product: In health education, the product is usually the health behavior targeted in the program you are offering, though it can also be an actual product as well. In the VERB campaign, the product was physical activity.
- Price: Often thought of as the cost to participate in the program, price in social marketing should be thought of much more broadly. What does it cost the customer to "buy" the product you are selling? In the case of the VERB campaign, the price of participating in physical activity can include the price of needed equipment (shoes, balls, swimsuits, admission to pools, jump ropes, etc.) but also the more indirect costs of time (time being physically active cannot also be spent sleeping, doing homework, etc.), safety (the risk of injury), and possible emotional stress (losing, failing at learning a new activity, etc.). It is the goal of the social marketing campaign to convince the customer that these costs are lower than the cost of NOT performing the behavior (that there are costs to being inactive—say, being out of shape or missing out on playing with your friends who are physically active) and to help the customer find ways to make the costs affordable. The VERB campaign made sure to include very low (financial) cost activities and gave away balls, jump ropes, and so on, to keep customer costs manageable.
- Place: Often in health education it is necessary to place messages where the behavior is to be performed. For example, when we get into our car and forget to put on the seat belt, the car usually makes a beeping noise to remind us to fasten our seat belt—which is more useful than, say, receiving a message reminding you to fasten your seat belt while you are

at the grocery store. Social marketing techniques require a careful consideration of where the behavior needs to be performed and where the consumer needs to be supported in adopting the behavior. In the VERB campaign, messages were placed on TV, radio, websites, and in-text messaging, as well as at schools, community events, and festivals—all "places" where tweens were.

■ Promotion: Promotion is probably the least understood of the four Ps. Often it is thought of as the advertising around a campaign, but it is better thought of as a collection of offerings—including advertising—designed to increase audience engagement with the target behavior. This can include giveaways of products necessary to perform the behavior, prizes, incentives, and so on. In the VERB campaign, promotions included giveaways, such as turnkey kits for schools and community groups and balls and other sports equipment, but also activities at sponsored events, online spaces where tweens could upload videos of themselves, and contests and sweepstakes.

The essential tenets, according to Andreasen (1995), of social marketing are the following:
1. Consumer behavior is the bottom line.
2. Programs must be cost effective.
3. All strategies begin with the customer.
4. Interventions involve the 4 Ps: product, price, place, and promotion.
5. Market research is essential to designing, pretesting, and evaluating intervention programs.
6. Markets are carefully segmented.
7. Competition is always recognized. (Andreasen, 1995, p. 14).

# ▶ HEALTH COMMUNICATION METHODS AND TECHNOLOGIES[7]

Today there is a dizzying number of channels (to use McGuire's term) though which messages can be relayed, and in fact the choice of the channel(s) is deeply tied to the message and the audience. Some channels are more appropriate for a certain audience, and some channels are less suited to deliver certain messages. For example, you might choose to promote handwashing through signs in a restroom but it would be less appropriate to, say, set up a hotline for questions about handwashing. Likewise, your audience's needs and preferences will drive channel selection. According to the Pew Internet and American Life Project, nearly two-thirds of people ages 18 to 29 used Snapchat in early 2021, but only 2% of those over 65 did so (Auxier & Anderson, 2021). Clearly, Snapchat would not be your first choice for a way to promote programs for seniors. In this section, we will review some of the methods of communication, including their pros and cons.

## HILL'S CRITERIA FOR CAUSATION

It is often observed that "correlation does not equal causation"—but how can causation be established? There are certainly multiple schools of thought on the issue, but Hill (1965) posited a set of nine criteria which provide evidence of causation, at least from the epidemiological perspective. These criteria are the following:

1. Strength: The larger the association, the more likely it is causal.

---

[7] Competency 6.6 Select methods and technologies used to deliver message(s), copyright of the National Commission for Health Education Credentialing, Inc. (NCHEC).

2. Consistency: Consistent findings observed by different persons in different places with different samples strengthen the likelihood that there is a causal relationship.
3. Specificity: The more specific an association is between a factor and an effect, the larger the chance of a causal relationship.
4. Temporality: The effect has to occur after the cause.
5. Biological gradient: (sometimes called *dose response*)—Greater exposure should generally lead to greater effect.
6. Plausibility: Does the relationship seem plausible?
7. Coherence: Coherence between epidemiological and laboratory findings increases the likelihood of an effect.
8. Experiment: Presence of experimental evidence.
9. Analogy: The effect of similar factors may be considered, for example, the effects of thalidomide when judging the effects of other drugs on birth defects.

Questions to ask to assess online health information (adapted from National Cancer Institute's [2002] *Making Health Communication Programs Work: A Planner's Guide*):

■ From whom is the information? It should be abundantly clear from the page who is responsible for the information. Individual authors may be listed, and if so, should include their credentials. Otherwise, information may be authored, but should be clearly marked as to whom the information is from.
■ Where does the funding come from? It should be clear who is funding the information. Many websites exist that have generic-sounding names but really are funded by groups with specific interests. A good place to look is the "About Us" section or an online search on what the organization is or whom it is funded by.
■ Is the organization the original source of information, or is it reposting someone else's information? All original source material should be clearly cited so you can judge whether it is up to date, relevant, and methodologically sound.
■ Is there a review process or information clearance process before information is posted? Most legitimate sources of health information have someone with medical, public health, or similar credentials review information to make sure it is correct. A search on the site should reveal what their process is, and who is in charge of reviewing information.
■ When was the information last updated or reviewed? The page should have a note indicating when it was last updated or had its information reviewed. Some topics have rapidly evolving information, so consider whether the information you are viewing is likely to have changed recently.
■ What is the site's privacy/use policy? This is very important, particularly if you are entering in information about any personal health topics.

## ▶ A WORD ABOUT DOMAIN NAMES

Many savvy health educators look at domain names (part of the URL or web address) as a way to assess where information is coming from. As a reminder, in the United States, a government agency has *.gov* in the address. An educational institution is indicated by *.edu* in the address. A professional organization such as a scientific or research society will be identified as *.org*. For example, the American Heart Association's website is www.heart.org. Commercial sites are identified by a *.com* or *.net* or *.biz* or a number of other domains. Research has shown that people tend to trust information from .gov and .edu websites the most, but remember, these are not hard-and-fast rules. Just because something has a .edu or .org domain name does not mean that the information is correct or free from bias. Domain names are simply one tool to help you determine who the information is from.

Following is a list of information resources that are generally considered trustworthy. This list is by no means exhaustive, and it is quite possible that even these reputable sources might make mistakes, but these are a good place to start.

## GOVERNMENTAL

The World Health Organization (www.who.int)—The World Health Organization's primary role is "to direct and coordinate international health within the United Nations' system."

U.S. Department of Health and Human Services (DHHS; www.dhhs.gov)—"The mission of the DHHS is to enhance and protect the health and well-being of all Americans. We fulfill that mission by providing for effective health and human services and fostering advances in medicine, public health, and social services."

Under DHHS, there are a number of health- and research-related organizations that are excellent sources of information.

- CDC (www.cdc.gov)
- Agency for Healthcare Research and Quality (www.ahrq.gov)
- Agency for Toxic Substances and Disease Registry (www.atsdr.cdc.gov)
- Centers for Medicare and Medicaid Services (www.cms.gov)
- Food and Drug Administration (www.fda.gov)
- Health Resources and Services Administration (www.hrsa.gov)
- Indian Health Services (www.ihs.gov)
- National Institutes of Health (www.nih.gov)
- Substance Abuse and Mental Health Services Administration (SAMHSA; www.samhsa.gov)

## ORGANIZATIONS

Community-based organizations (CBOs) or nongovernmental organizations (NGOs; a term more commonly used internationally) can be excellent sources of information—or not. All the same caveats listed earlier apply when assessing their information. Examples of highly trusted information include the following:

- American Heart Association (www.heart.org)
- American Cancer Society (www.cancer.org)
- American Red Cross (www.redcross.org)
- American Public Health Association (www.apha.org)
- Society for Public Health Educators (www.sophe.org)

Foundations can also be a wonderful source of reputable health information. It is important with them, as with other organizations, to understand their motives, funding, and methods. The Foundation Center (www.foundationcenter.org) can help you become familiar with foundations that you might need to investigate. Examples of commonly cited foundations include the following:

- The Robert Wood Johnson Foundation (www.rwjf.org)
- The Henry J. Kaiser Family Foundation (www.kff.org)
- The Pew Internet and American Life Project (www.pewinternet.org)

Policy or research centers ("think tanks") are organizations devoted to advancing policies or research in a particular area or topic. Given that they often have an agenda of some kind, you should be aware of their funding and motivation, but they can be highly valued information sources. Examples of such centers who do work in public health are the following:

- Rand Corporation (www.rand.org)
- The Pew Research Center (www.pewresearch.org)
- RTI International (www.rti.org)

Finally, there are a number of searchable databases for health information. These may contain access to journals, white papers, abstracts, evidence-based programs, and databases. Some of them require subscriptions, which may be available through workplaces, local libraries, or professional organizations. Some examples are the following:

Cumulative Index to Nursing and Allied Health Literature (CINAHL): The CINAHL database accesses nursing and allied health literature covering a wide range of topics including nursing, biomedicine, health sciences librarianship, alternative/complementary medicine, consumer health, and 17 allied health disciplines. Membership is required. Available at www.CINAHL.com.

- Evidence-Based Medicine Reviews (EBMR): The EBMR is a collection of databases that contain evidence-based strategies, program, and clinical information including the Cochrane Database of Systematic Reviews. Some information is available for free, others require a fee. Available at www.ovid.com

- Education Resource Information Center (ERIC): The ERIC has journals related to school health, school-aged children, and education generally. It is free to use (full-text articles may require payment). Available at https://eric.ed.gov

- MEDLINE: One of the go-to-sources for medical and public health data. PubMed provides free access to the database, though accessing the full text of certain articles may not be free. Available at www.ncbi.nlm.nih.gov/pubmed

- PsycINFO: As the name suggests, this database contains journal articles, abstracts, books, white papers, and dissertations related to psychology and behavioral science. There is a fee. Available at www.apa.org/pubs/databases/psycinfo

## SOURCES OF EVIDENCE-BASED PROGRAMS

Many health educators will want to be familiar with sources of evidence-based programs, or programs that have been shown to be reliable and valid (at least for certain populations). Following are common places to find evidence-based programs:

- Community Health Online Resource Center (https://www.cdc.gov/nccdphp/dch/online-resource/index.htm)

- Effective Interventions: HIV Prevention that Works (https://www.cdc.gov/hiv/ effective-interventions/index.html)
- Healthy People 2020 Evidence-based Resources (www.healthypeople.gov/2020/ tools-resources/Evidence-Based-Resources)
- SAMHSA's National Registry of Evidence-based Programs and Practices (www.samhsa. gov/resource-search/ebp)
- U.S. Preventive Services Task Force (www.uspreventiveservicestaskforce.org)
- The Community Guide (www.thecommunityguide.org/task-force-findings)

# ▶ DEVELOP MESSAGES AND MATERIALS

Once you have gathered reliable information and chosen the appropriate channel(s) to reach your audience, you must develop your messages and materials. Obviously, the way you do this will depend largely on what channel you have selected and the content you need to deliver. Use your needs assessment, including any literature reviews you may have done, and select good theoretical underpinnings based on behavioral change and communication theory.

Depending on the channel you chose, you may need to engage with production professionals, such as graphic designers or television or audio producers to create your materials. Or you may need to produce them yourself, perhaps with the help of software such as Adobe InDesign, iMovie, or Adobe Audition. Or you may select online graphic design applications such as Canva.com. Your materials should be assessed along the way to ensure they are appropriate and understandable to your audience. Consider accessibility, such as whether your infographic is useable by someone with color blindness, and make sure any online information you provide is compliant with Section 508 of the Rehabilitation Act ("508 Compliant") so it can be read by screen readers for the visually-impaired, and caption any audio material, such as video or podcast, so people with hearing loss can read what is being said.

Of course, accessibility is critical to consider throughout your development process. Remember to write using plain language principles (see Chapter 7).

Below are some resources to ensure materials are accessible:

- Website Accessibility Evaluation (WAVE) Tool is a free tool that helps ensure that websites are accessible to those with disabilities (https://wave.webaim.org).
- Coblis—Colorblindness Simulator allows you to upload images and see how they would look to people with varying types of color blindness (https://www.color-blindness.com/ coblis-color-blindness-simulator/).
- CDC Clear Communication Index: The CDC Clear Communication Index (Index) is a research-based tool to help you develop and assess public communication materials (https://www.cdc.gov/ccindex/index.html).
- Suitability Assessment of Materials (SAM) instrument provides a worksheet to review materials on their content, literacy demand, graphic design, learning stimulation, and cultural appropriateness.

As with any implementation, you should seek formative evaluation (see Chapter 5) to get feedback on your materials, preferably with representatives of the intended audience. Edit your materials based on the information you gain during pretesting and keep pretesting until you are satisfied that the materials meet the objectives and the needs of the audience. Pilot testing can also be done to launch the materials in a limited way to check for acceptability and suitability.

# ▶ DISSEMINATE MESSAGES AND MATERIALS[8]

Once the materials are developed and tested, it is time to launch them. Here, as always, a thorough knowledge of your audience is appropriate, whether you are providing the information to the population or key stakeholders. While it is often obvious who the populations are you are working with, take a minute to review who the potential stakeholders you might need to remember:

- Program management and staff
- Funders (or those you fund)
- Coalitions/advocacy programs who are interested in your topic (local, regional, state, national)
- Health departments (local, state)
- Schools or educational organizations (local, county, regional, or state)
- Universities or research organizations
- Government (local, county, or state)
- Businesses, chambers of commerce, or other commercial organizations
- Healthcare systems, insurers, clinicians
- Religious organizations or CBOs
- Neighborhood associations or groups
- Law enforcement/justice system
- Population-specific organizations such as a local organization serving the blind or Latinos

If you are not thoroughly familiar with the population or partner and their preferred methods of receiving information, it is helpful to find someone who is and discuss what would be the best methods for disseminating the information. Typically, health educators use a wide variety of dissemination methods, including:

- Presentations
- Lectures
- Demonstrations (cooking classes, shopping trips, or baby care classes)
- Printed educational materials (posters, brochures, fact sheets, or infographics)
- Electronic information (webpages, social media posts, videos, interactive graphics, or video games)

Often, more than one technique will be called for, particularly if the information is complex, important, or being presented to various audiences. Utilize your key informants to make sure that your choices, language, visuals, tone, and engagement level are appropriate and acceptable to your audiences, and ask for and be open to feedback.

## *New Media and Other Innovative Tools*

Communicating about health in the 21st century almost certainly will require an active knowledge of new media, which can be an important way to engage with your audience, monitor and correct mis- or disinformation, and disseminate your messages widely. Web 2.0 is a term that refers to websites that are interactive (rather than didactic), easy to use, scalable, and can perform in a variety of ways. According to Wikipedia (itself an example

---

[8] Competency 6.7 Deliver the message(s) effectively using the identified media and strategies, copyright of the National Commission for Health Education Credentialing, Inc. (NCHEC).

of Web 2.0 principles), "A Web 2.0 site may allow users to interact and collaborate with each other in a social media dialogue as creators of user-generated content in a virtual community, in contrast to websites, where people are limited to the passive viewing of content. Examples of Web 2.0 include social networking sites, blogs, wikis, folksonomies, video-sharing sites, hosted services, Web applications, collaborative consumption platforms, and mashups" (en .wikipedia.org/wiki/Web_2.0). In the following section, we review some of the most used new media and highlight how they might be—or have been—used in health campaigns. The Pew Internet and American Life Project (www.pewinternet.org) has the latest statistics and figures on who is doing what on the internet and should be a first step for health educators considering the internet as a channel for message delivery.

Social networking sites, such as Facebook, Twitter, Instagram, Snapchat, and TikTok, offer users a way to interact with others who have common interests and/or social networks. They are among the most commonly used new media, boasting, in Facebook's case, nearly three billion registered users. Different populations tend to frequent different social media sites—women, for example, are much more frequent users of Pinterest than men, and African Americans and Latinos are overrepresented on Twitter and Instagram.

There are specific social media sites that may have relevance to a health educator, including:

- Academia.edu—for academics and researchers
- CaringBridge—for patients and caregivers of those with serious medical conditions
- Doximity—for medical professionals
- PatientsLikeMe—for patients with serious medical conditions

Internationally, there are many different social media sites, and some of the most popular in the United States may not even be available in other countries. As always, understanding your audience and knowing where they get their information and who they trust, is critical to good health communication.

Pros: Social media sites are popular, easy to use, and can reach a wide number of people. It is also possible to pay to advertise on many of them to target information to different demographics, say, women between 25 and 40 or men who live in the southeastern United States. Users often help to spread your message by retweeting, forwarding, or sharing messages. Social media channels also provide instant feedback from your audience in the forms of comments and activity. They are also easily evaluated for process measures—users usually have access to information about how many people have seen (reach) your message, how often they have seen your message (dose), and how often they have interacted with a message (engagement).

Cons: It can be hard to know exactly who is getting your message, and you only have feedback from those who chose to give it. The 24/7 nature of these channels requires careful and nearly constant monitoring to ensure that comments posted are acceptable to the message sender and to ensure that the message is being received as intended. Mis- and disinformation spread rapidly and effectively through social media and can pose a significant threat to public health interventions, as we have seen with vaccines and COVID-19. **Blogs**, or weblogs, are online journals that can be accessed by anyone with an internet connection. They provide a more in-depth way to explore a topic, as they are not limited by number of characters. Blogs can be written by an individual or come from an organization and be authored by different people. They often include a comment section where readers can interact with the author and others.

Pros: A blog gives the author an unlimited amount of space to write. Blogs can easily accommodate different ways of communication by including videos, pictures, audio, links to other web pages, interactive formats, and so on. They are a good place for discussion or to teach or explain more complex information and are often read by people with a deeper interest in the given topic who are looking for significant amounts of information.

Cons: Content has to be seen and considered interesting by readers to get them to read it. Competing for eyes with all the other information available out there is a challenge, especially in trying to engage readers with limited literacy skills or attention spans. Readers expect frequent updating, and developing content is a time-consuming task.

## ▶ MOBILE TECHNOLOGIES

Mobile (or cell) phones are one of the fastest growing technologies in the world. According to the Pew Internet and American Life Survey (www.pewinternet.org) from June 2021, 95% of American adults owned a cell phone and 85% owned a smartphone. Cell phones, and particularly smartphones, are increasingly being used as ways to connect with users, be it through mobile apps (applications [computer programs] that work specifically on a smartphone) for social networking sites; health apps, which can track physical activity, biometric information such as blood pressure or blood sugar levels, or other health information; or text messaging. Over 80% of Americans text message, and programs such as Text4Baby (www.text4baby.org) utilize text message functions to deliver timely, targeted health information to users. However, less than 10% of Americans use text-based health alerts.

## ▶ EVALUATING COMMUNICATIONS[9]

As with all interventions, communication messages, materials, and campaigns should be evaluated to ensure fidelity and to understand their impact. We've already covered evaluation in Chapter 5, and the same types of evaluations can be done with communications: process evaluations track the fidelity to the implementation, the reach of the material (number of times it has been seen), and any problems that arise. Impact evaluations will measure how much change there was in the audience after they have seen a material: Did they gain knowledge? Change an attitude? Perform a behavior? Depending on where you are deploying your messages and materials, it may be easier or harder to answer those questions. For instance, if you are teaching a class where you show a video, you can test changes there. How much knowledge or attitude change you get from advertisements on the bus may be harder to assess, and will depend on your level of resources to do so. For that reason, outcome evaluation on communication messages and materials is fairly rare, and nearly always confined to large, well-funded programs. CDC's Tips from Former Smokers and "the truth®" anti-tobacco campaign are two examples of programs with a thorough outcomes evaluation. New media comes with a variety of process tools baked into them. Most web-based or social media platforms have a number of analytical features available to content owners and can help you understand the reach and spread of your messages. Comment sections can provide information about how materials are being received and provide a way for the audience to report problems or concerns. However, analytics alone may not be enough to gauge the full impact of your materials. As with all other kinds of evaluation, do as much as you can with what you have—any evaluation is better than nothing.

---

[9] Competency 6.8 Evaluate communication, copyright of the National Commission for Health Education Credentialing, Inc. (NCHEC).

# ▶ CONCLUSION

Communication is a huge part of a health educator's job. Whether communication is taking a primary or secondary role in your intervention, it is important to remember that communication is a program, and as such, it needs to have all the same steps followed that you would with any other program. In Chapter 8, you will review Area VII: Leadership and Management.

1. A health educator has identified an emerging issue that is affecting the health of people in her community. She believes she needs to create some communication materials to help address conditions that are exacerbating the health condition. What would be her next step?

   **A.** Gather information about the health topic from reliable resources
   **B.** Set goals and objectives
   **C.** Join a coalition of organizations and people interested in the health topic
   **D.** Draft a letter to state lawmakers

2. In social marketing, this "P" is the behavior you are trying to get your audience to do, the services you provide, or the objects you offer.

   **A.** Product
   **B.** Price
   **C.** Promotion
   **D.** Perceived benefit

3. In social marketing, this "P" is the communication messages, materials, channels, or activities you use to get your message to your audience:

   **A.** Product
   **B.** Price
   **C.** Promotion
   **D.** Perceived benefit

4. When developing a health communication intervention, prioritizing target audience segment(s) allows you to:

   **A.** Tailor messages for all segments
   **B.** Avoid spreading your resources too thin
   **C.** Address secondary audiences
   **D.** Be certain that no group is left out

5. A health educator working in a community center is developing a social media campaign to encourage seniors to be physically active. She has segmented her audience into three groups: inactive "Super Seniors" (those older than 80 years); active, younger, female seniors (65–75); and those who have recently reduced their activity after a health event. After matching each high-priority audience segment with current and desired behaviors, the next step is to narrow her audience/behavior pairs based on:

   **A.** The ability to identify an antecedent behavior
   **B.** The presence of a social determinant of health
   **C.** Risk, impact, behavioral, resource, and political feasibility
   **D.** The likelihood of creating a permanent lifestyle change

## 1. A) Gather information about the health topic from reliable resources
After identifying a health topic, the second step would be to gather information about the health topic from reliable resources. These can include peer-reviewed journals, federal or state repositories of vital statistics, reputable nongovernmental organization (NGO) sources, or primary data.

## 2. A) Product
The product is the target behavior you are trying to get your audience to adopt or maintain. It can also be an object or service you are implementing as part of your program. In the Truth Campaign to End Youth Smoking, the product was feeling rebellious, in control, and "cool" by attacking adults who try to manipulate teens into smoking.

## 3. C) Promotion
Promotion is the messages, channels, or activities you use to get your audience to adopt the target behavior. These can include traditional TV, social media, radio spots, brochures, posters, and so on, or objects they can use when performing the behavior, such as water bottles for encouraging physical activity. In the Truth Campaign, the promotion included TV, internet, and billboard ads with messages that appealed to youth's desire to be in control and oppositional to adult authority figures with questionable motives.

## 4. B) Avoid spreading your resources too thin
Prioritizing target audiences allows you to use program resources where they will be most effective.

## 5. C) Risk, impact, behavioral, resource, and political feasibility
In deciding what segments of the audience to target for intervention, a health educator must examine what health risks each segment faces, how likely it is that "the needle can be moved" on the population (some populations are easier to change than others), the resources available to implement a change, and how acceptable an intervention is going to be politically and to the population. All of these decisions go into planning which segments of the population are going to receive attention and resources and which are lower priority, either because of need or because they are too difficult or expensive to work with.

6. A major challenge of developing persuasive messages is:

   A. They are inherently unethical
   B. Identifying the most effective channel, context, and message content
   C. Finding enough statistics to make a convincing argument
   D. The limited number of techniques that exist for evaluating the message's effectiveness

7. Which of the following is least likely to be true?

   A. Using plain language is desirable in communicating with the public
   B. Communicating facts clearly to the public is more important than communicating clearly to professionals
   C. Using plain language is desirable in communicating to an academic audience
   D. Tailoring your message to your audience will improve your communication

8. All channels of communication have their advantages and disadvantages. Which of the following channels is most likely to have credibility and access among its chief limitations?

   A. Television
   B. Blogs
   C. Newspapers
   D. Peer-reviewed journals

9. All of the following are advantages of using television as a channel for communicating health information except:

   A. Can reach low-income audiences
   B. It has the largest audience reach
   C. It is flexible and inexpensive
   D. Messages can be controlled

10. Approximately what percentage of Americans are considered "proficient" in terms of health literacy?

    A. 2%
    B. 12%
    C. 22%
    D. 32%

11. Which of the following is NOT a strategy for creating readable materials?

    A. Keep sentences short
    B. Use the passive voice
    C. Use headings and subheadings
    D. Justify the left margin

12. Which of the following is most likely to state reliable, unbiased health information?

    A. An article in a popular magazine
    B. A brochure from a health foods company
    C. A website from a pharmaceutical company
    D. A peer-reviewed journal article

## 6. B) Identifying the most effective channel, context, and message content

Evaluations have shown that persuasive messages can be very effective at changing behavior and can be done ethically. And certainly for a variety of topics, there is a wealth of statistics available, though presenting people with statistics is not always very persuasive (we all know that tobacco kills thousands of people a year, yet many Americans still smoke). Finding the right mix of channels, places and times, and content of messages that will ultimately change people's behaviors is an enduring problem for creating persuasive messages, since one mix may be effective for some audience members but not for others.

## 7. B) Communicating facts clearly to the public is more important than communicating clearly to professionals

Material should be communicated clearly to any audience, regardless if the audience comprises professionals or the general public.

## 8. B) Blogs

Electronic media do many things well, but divides still remain in terms of access, and the credibility of electronic media can be harder to establish.

## 9. C) It is flexible and inexpensive

Unless it is free media (such as an interview on a news program), television is a very expensive medium. Because of high production and airtime costs, a limited number of messages can be created and shown.

## 10. B) 12%

Only 12% of Americans are in the "proficient" category.

## 11. B) Use the passive voice

Keeping sentences short, using headings, judicious use of white space, and justifying the left margin (not centered or right-justified text) as people are used to reading, all help increase readability. The use of the passive voice generally creates extra words to read and can confuse readers as to your meaning (such as in this sentence!).

## 12. D) A peer-reviewed journal article

While all can be interesting and possibly appropriate sources of information, the information gained from a peer-reviewed journal article is most likely to be accurate, reliable, and unbiased. However, mistakes and even bias do happen in the peer-reviewed literature as well, which is why we consider the preponderance of evidence there and not just the findings of individual studies.

**13.** The following are important components of health literacy except:

    **A.** Cultural competency
    **B.** Ability to navigate systems
    **C.** Functional literacy
    **D.** Innate intelligence

**14.** A social worker at a hospital has developed a packet of information and a list of resources for families of people struggling with addiction. He wants to make sure that the information and resources are understandable and helpful to families. Rank in order, from most helpful to least helpful, the activities below that he could use to understand if his information and resources will be helpful to the families he is trying to reach.

| | |
|---|---|
| **1.** Hold several focus groups or formalized testing with families of people with addiction to drugs or alcohol to discuss the materials and receive feedback. | **A.** 1, 2, 3, 4, 5 <br> **B.** 2, 1, 3, 4, 5 <br> **C.** 5, 4, 3, 2, 1 <br> **D.** 2, 1, 5, 4, 3 |

    **2.** Show the materials to a couple of families as he encounters them in the course of his duties, and solicit feedback.

    **3.** Show them to coworkers who have knowledge of the target population, and solicit their feedback.

    **4.** Use the reading-level analyzer on his word-processing software and revise until the level is at eighth grade or below.

    **5.** Do nothing.

**15.** A health educator is tracking how many trainings her staff has conducted and how many copies of educational materials they have sent out as part of the campaign to ensure that children with asthma are being identified and treated. What type of evaluation are these activities?

    **A.** Formative
    **B.** Process
    **C.** Outcome
    **D.** Impact

**16.** How many Americans have basic or below basic levels of health literacy?

    **A.** 7 million
    **B.** 27 million
    **C.** 47 million
    **D.** 77 million

*(See answers next page.)*

### 13. D) Innate intelligence
Health literacy is "the degree to which individuals have the capacity to obtain, process, and understand basic health information and services needed to make appropriate health decisions." Health literacy is dependent on both individual ability and systematic factors, including a person's ability to read (functional literacy), do math (numeracy), navigate the healthcare system, and navigate culture. It does not dependent on innate intelligence—many highly intelligent people have low levels of health literacy.

### 14. A) 1, 2, 3, 4, 5
In a perfect world, you would be able to hold a series of focus groups (or formalized testing if confidentiality is a concern) and really test the materials with family members of people with addiction to drugs or alcohol. Materials are made better with thorough testing, revision, and retesting. However, in the real world, we often lack time and resources for such testing, so an alternative such as asking (in a professionally appropriate way) for feedback from members of a culture may have to substitute for formal testing.

### 15. B) Process
Monitoring and evaluating the implementation of a campaign is process evaluation.

### 16. D) 77 million
More than a third of adults were in the basic (47 million) and below basic (30 million) health literacy groups. These adults can read a pamphlet or a short list of instructions, respectively, but may not be able to read and understand instructions on a prescription label.

17. Which of the following are least likely to be able to be accomplished via a program that is entirely communication-based?

    A. Teach elementary school children to read and interpret nutrition labels
    B. Persuade a group of seniors that they should ask their healthcare providers about a shingles vaccine
    C. Increase the percentage of nurses who wash their hands every time upon entering a patient's room
    D. Promote physical activity in a rural high school population by encouraging students to walk to school

18. Which SMART objective component is missing from the following statement: "By the end of the program, grandparents will report putting their grandchildren to sleep on their backs 100% of the time."

    A. Measurable
    B. Time-sensitive
    C. Attainable
    D. Realistic

19. If a health educator is reviewing whether the expenditures for his educational campaign are within the budget he set, what kind of evaluation is he doing?

    A. Formative
    B. Process
    C. Impact
    D. Outcome

20. Tracking "likes" and "shares" of a message is an example of what kind of communication indicator?

    A. Recall
    B. Dose
    C. Engagement
    D. Reach

**17. D) Promote physical activity in a rural high school population by encouraging students to walk to school**

Communication is a powerful tool, but it cannot make up for lack of resources and services, or overcome physical barriers. In a rural area, many students will live miles from school and there are often neither sidewalks nor crosswalks to ensure student safety. Other methods would have to be employed to bring about an increase in physical activity.

**18. A) Measurable**

The objective is not measurable because it does not specify how many grandparents will achieve the goal. Without that information, we cannot measure the impact or potential change to expect—if only one grandparent changes their behavior, it is unlikely to have a substantial change. The goal is also not specific because it does not mention the age of the grandchildren, and only infants need to be placed to sleep on their backs.

**19. B) Process**

Process indicators include those that monitor how closely the program is being implanted to the program plan. These can include dose and reach as well as budget.

**20. C) Engagement**

Engagement is the number of people who interact with the message online in some direct way, such as liking, sharing, or commenting.

# REFERENCES

Agency for Healthcare Research and Quality. (2020, September.) *Use the teach-back method: Tool #5.* https://www.ahrq.gov/health-literacy/improve/precautions/tool5.html

Andreasen, A. R. (1995). *Marketing social change: Changing behavior to promote health, social development, and the environment.* Jossey-Bass.

Auxier, B., & Anderson, M. (2021, April 7). Social media use in 2021. *Pew Research Center.* https://www.pewresearch.org/internet/2021/04/07/social-media-use-in-2021/

Centers for Disease Control and Prevention. (2010). *Youth media campaign: VERB, it's what we do.* http://www.cdc.gov/youthcampaign

Hawkins, R. P., Kreuter, M., Resnicow, K., Fishbein, M., & Dijkstra, A. (2008). Understanding tailoring in communicating about health. *Health Education Research, 23*(3), 454–466. https://doi.org/10.1093/her/cyn004

Hernandez, E. L., Dietrich, S. L., & Bauman, K. J. (2022). What languages does the United States speak? A geographic analysis of the languages spoken at home in the United States, 2015-2019 [Poster]. Proceedings of the Annual meeting of the Population Association of America, April 2022. https://www.census.gov/content/dam/Census/library/visualizations/2022/demo/Poster%20PAA%202022%20Language%20Geographic%20Distribution_20220323.pdf

Hill, A. B. (1965). The environment and disease: Association or causation? *Proceedings of the Royal Society of Medicine, 58*(5), 295-300.

Lefebvre, R. C., & Flora, J. A. (1988). Social marketing and public health intervention. *Health Education Quarterly, 15,* 299–315. 10.1177/109019818801500305

National Center for Education Statistics. (2006). *The health literacy of America's adults: Results from the 2003 National Assessment of adult literacy.* U.S. Department of Education.

Office of Disease Prevention and Health Promotion. (n.d.). Health literacy. In *Healthy People 2030. U.S. Department of Health and Human Services.* https://health.gov/our-work/national-health-initiatives/healthy-people/healthy-people-2030/health-literacy-healthy-people-2030

# Area of Responsibility VII: Leadership and Management[1]

## ▶ INTRODUCTION

This chapter covers two different but related topics concerning health education: leadership and management. Effective leadership and management are complex and highlight the important roles of health educators. Building on your leadership and management skills is essential to the delivery of high health education standards, including program development, implementation, evaluation, and research and practice. To meet the health education needs of our communities in the 21st century, we need competent leaders with management skills who can help coordinate relationships and train and prepare future health educators while overseeing human resources, managing financial and program resources, and planning for the future. This chapter briefly considers the current leadership theories and explores leadership and management skills, roles, and practices within the context of health education.

Similar to Chapter 3's focus on planning and coalition building, effective leadership and management skills require developing relationships with partners, teams, and committees. For example, you may lead efforts to ensure that health education and promotion programs are delivered with fidelity. Leaders also bring partners and stakeholders together through meetings, joint learning activities, and direct service delivery. Management skills will require communicating with partners and stakeholders about hiring, training, conducting performance reviews, and securing and overseeing the management of budgets, technologies, and other resources. Leaders in health education and promotion are also often required to have the competence to facilitate, negotiate, and collaborate in increasingly competitive environments (Wright et al., 2000).[2]

Often, you may need to identify partners and community/coalition members from schools, lawmakers, law enforcement, and community professionals from relevant public and community organizations with similar interests in health education. These members should be able to participate in shared decision-making, engage in communication, and collaborate on the proposed health education activities/programs. It is crucial to engage these members in the planning and implementation of program-related and organizational goals (Rowitz, 2014).

---

[1] The Eight Areas of Responsibility for Health Education Specialists are copyright of the National Commission for Health Education Credentialing, Inc. (NCHEC).

[2] Competency 7.1 Coordinate relationships with partners and stakeholders (e.g., individuals, teams, coalitions, and committees), copyright of the National Commission for Health Education Credentialing, Inc. (NCHEC).

## KEY TERMS FOR LEADERSHIP AND MANAGEMENT IN HEALTH EDUCATION

**Leadership**—Involves bringing partners and stakeholders together by establishing a clear vision and mission that incorporates values, beliefs, ethics, and strategies that align with personal and organizational goals (Wright et al., 2003).

**Teamwork**—Involves coordination and effective communication that aids in team-building and works to address common goals (Wright et al., 2000).

**Mission** – Often is a short or long statement about the purpose of the health education organization or program including values, actions, and links to present and/or future goals (Rowitz, 2014). Mission statements often follow from the vision statement by outlining a process for how the vision will be achieved, such as providing more detail-oriented, concrete, and tangible steps. *Please see examples in Chapter 3.*

**Vision**—Typically reflects the mission statement and highlights leaders' views for the health education organization/program's future (Rowitz, 2014). Vision statements are often based on personal values, beliefs, and capture our sense of our ultimate purpose or calling in life. *Please see examples in Chapter 3.*

**Organizational development**—Term that reflects the strategies and interventions aimed at building skills of partners, stakeholders, and the organization to ensure that personal and organizational goals can be achieved (Wright et al., 2003).

**Strategic Planning**—This involves a phase of planning and reviewing values, mission and vision, and goals and objectives to ensure partners, stakeholders, and the organization can work to develop a plan, including a timeline, for achieving health education, promotion program-related, and organizational goals (Rowitz, 2014).

Leaders need to be committed to lifelong learning and personal growth. In terms of personal development, Rowitz (2014) has emphasized seven R's of self-esteem.

## SEVEN R'S OF SELF-ESTEEM APPLIED TO LEADERSHIP AND MANAGEMENT

1. **Respect**—Emphasizes the need for respect and trust in your partners and employees.
2. **Responsibility and Resources**—Highlights the importance of encouraging creativity and delegating essential tasks while allowing partners and employees some autonomy in completing these tasks.
3. **Risk-taking**—Plays an important role in driving innovation and is often necessary.
4. **Rewards and Recognition**—leaders need to ensure that partners and employees are recognized for their accomplishments. This can be an important motivator and driver of future successes.
5. **Relationships**—Are a key component of successful leadership. Leadership should focus on both the quality and quantity of personal relationships.
6. **Role-modeling**—Is an excellent way to promote co-learning, and it is another way to emphasize the practices and values important to an organization.
7. **Renewal**—Leaders should take advantage of opportunities for ongoing self-reflection, personal growth, and lifelong learning.

## ▶ PREPARING AND TRAINING OTHERS TO PROVIDE HEALTH EDUCATION AND PROMOTION PROGRAMMING[3]

Health educators often need to lead, train, and manage others to deliver health education and promotion programs. They may also need to be able to analyze, tailor, deliver, and evaluate the training of others (Lockyer, 1998). A needs assessment is an integral part of understanding gaps and training needs of health educators and the communities they serve. The needs assessment aims to improve knowledge and ensure that staff are prepared and that those being trained truly benefit. There are two major categories of training needs assessments: (a) self-assessments and (b) group assessments. A health educator can deliver them via a survey before training staff (or whoever is being trained; Lockyer, 1998).

The following topics should be considered in a training needs assessment survey (Joly et al., 2018):

- Background of participants, including position, role, length of time in current role
- National Commission for Health Education Credentialing (NCHEC)-related Competencies, such as skills in planning, implementing, and evaluating health education and promotion programs
- Topic areas or current health education programming needs
- Training modality preferences (in-person, online, hybrid, etc.)
- Technology capacities and access
- Barriers and facilitators

Incorporate principles of cultural humility when developing and delivering tailored training and health education and promotion programming so that it is appropriate and respectful to the communities we serve. We all must commit to self-reflection and self-critique, such as identifying and examining our own patterns of unintentional and intentional racism and classism, power imbalances, and establishing and maintaining mutually beneficial and equitable relationships (Greene-Moton & Minkler, 2020). Consider several key areas for health education specialists striving to ensure training, health education, and promotion programs are culturally appropriate:

**Knowledge:** Understanding the social determinants of health and health inequities.
**Attitudes:** Acknowledging conscious and subconscious stereotyping and bias and recognizing power and privilege.
**Skills:** Communicating nonhierarchically, identifying power imbalances, and facilitating shared decision-making and power.

See Chapter 9 for more information on cultural competence and related principles.

Health education specialists will also be responsible for evaluating their trainings. Please see Chapter 5 for more details on *Area of Responsibility IV: Evaluation and Research*. Key components of your evaluation of trainings include (a) engaging stakeholders; (b) describing the program; (c) focusing the evaluation design (e.g., questions, data collection procedures, and protocols); (d) gathering credible evidence (collecting data and answering evaluation questions); (e) justifying conclusions through data analysis, summarization, and interpretation; and (f) using and sharing lessons learned back with participants (Koplan et al., 1999).

---

[3] Competency 7.2 Prepare others to provide health education and promotion, copyright of the National Commission for Health Education Credentialing, Inc. (NCHEC).

# ▶ MANAGING PEOPLE[4]

Managing people and human resources for health education and promotion can be a serious challenge for health education specialists. Managing people often requires skills in the following (Orton et al., 2006):

- Project management
- Organizing complex projects and teams
- Directing and delegating tasks
- Communication and conflict management skills
- Managing teams and group dynamics
- Allocating resources to support project and program activities

Human resources management includes recruitment, interviewing, hiring, firing, performance appraisals, employee retention, understanding health and retirement benefit offerings, and being aware of federal, state, and local employment requirements (Rowitz, 2014). In addition, managers may be responsible for protecting confidentiality around conflicts and workplace challenges, supporting relationships with employees and their supervisors, and addressing job-related conflicts and harassment situations.

Recruitment of staff also requires unique skills in developing job descriptions and access to current technologies for recruitment. Online resources such as LinkedIn, Indeed, Emory University's Public Health Jobs Connection (https://apps.sph.emory.edu/PHEC/), SOPHE Career HUB (https://sophe.careerwebsite.com/), as well as NCHEC (www.nchec.org/job-postings) offer posting locations for jobs.

# ▶ MANAGING BUDGETS AND FINANCIAL RESOURCES[5]

Grants, contracts, and cooperative agreements are often used to fund health education and promotion programs. Health education specialists will be responsible for developing and monitoring budgets and financial-related planning and ensuring that grant and contract deliverables are met. In addition, it is vital to consider the potential value of health education and promotion services in terms of economic benefits, such as costs, benefits, and return-on-investment (ROI).

Budget preparation is a skill that takes practice. Budget planning should consider staff, volunteers, materials, equipment, technology, facility costs, additional resources, and budget needs. Grant budgets typically are made up of direct and indirect costs. Direct costs typically include salaries and wages, fringe benefits, consultant costs, equipment, supplies, travel, other expenses, and contractual costs. Fringe benefits are usually applicable to direct salaries and wages and average around 25% to 30%. Fringe benefits cover the costs of retirement, health insurance, workers' compensation, and federal payroll tax, such as the Federal Insurance Contributions Act (FICA). Indirect costs are limited to funding organization guidelines and/or negotiated rates. These indirect costs are comprised of expenses related to the general operation of the organization and activities, such as facilities and maintenance, utilities, internet, phone lines, and audits, accounting, and human resource personnel. Please see

---

[4] Competency 7.3 Manage human resources, copyright of the National Commission for Health Education Credentialing, Inc. (NCHEC).

[5] Competency 7.4 Manage fiduciary and material resources, copyright of the National Commission for Health Education Credentialing, Inc. (NCHEC).

examples from the Centers for Disease Control and Prevention (CDC): www.cdc.gov/hiv/pdf/funding/announcements/ps15-1509/ps15-1509-budget-preparation-guidelines.pdf.

There are several resources available to health education specialists in terms of grants and contract resources:

- Centers for Disease Control and Prevention Grants
  www.cdc.gov/grants/index.html
- Prevention and Public Health Fund
  www.hhs.gov/open/prevention/funding-opportunities/index.html
- Human Resources and Services Administration—Health Workforce
  bhw.hrsa.gov/funding/apply-grant
- Area Health Education Centers
  www.grants.gov/web/grants/view-opportunity.html?oppId=334468
- Association for Prevention Teaching and Research
  www.aptrweb.org/page/grants
- Coordinated Approach to Child Health
  catch.org/news-resources/grant-finder/
- Society for Public Health Education
  www.sophe.org/about/awards-fellowships-scholarships/

## ▶ STRATEGIC PLANNING[6]

Strategic planning is necessary to develop, implement, and sustain health education and promotion programs. Strategic planning brings leaders and stakeholders together to design a plan to ensure the success of health education and promotion organizations. **Strategic planning** involves a process of planning and reviewing values, mission and vision, and goals and objectives to ensure partners, stakeholders, and the organization can work to develop a plan, including a timeline, for achieving health education and promotion program-related goals and the organization's overall future efforts (Rowitz, 2014). Health education specialists must gather information about internal and external environments, discuss the organization's future, and develop organizational goals and ways to measure progress on these goals.

Two common models used in strategic planning among health education and health science-related fields are the Assessment Protocol for Excellence in Public Health (APEX*PH*) approach to assessment and the Mobilizing for Action through Planning and Partnerships (MAPP) model (Rowitz, 2014).

The APEX*PH* approach has three parts (Rowitz, 2014). Part 1 involves the following eight-step Organizational Capacity Assessment:

1. Prepare for the Organizational Capacity Assessment.
2. Score indicators for importance and current status.
3. Identify strengths and weaknesses.
4. Analyze and report strengths.
5. Analyze weaknesses.
6. Rank problems in order of priority.
7. Develop and implement action plans.
8. Institutionalize the assessment process.

---

[6] Competency 7.5 Conduct strategic planning with appropriate stakeholders, copyright of the National Commission for Health Education Credentialing, Inc. (NCHEC).

Part 2 of the APEX*PH* approach involves the Community Process, where key members of a community and organizational staff assess the community's health and identify how to tie the health education and program efforts to community strengths and health problems (Rowitz, 2014). Both objective health data and community perceptions of community health problems are useful in this part. Part 3 involves Completing the Cycle, where the organization integrates the findings from Part 1's Organizational Capacity Assessment and Part 2's Community Process into the ongoing health education and promotion activities to best meet the needs of their community; it also ties to the policy development, assurance, monitoring, and evaluation plans developed during Parts 1 and 2 (Rowitz, 2014).

MAPP was developed by the CDC and NACCHO (National Association of County and City Health Officials) in 2001 as a community-based strategic planning model to address the health of communities and public health systems (Rowitz, 2014). MAPP provides a framework for prioritizing public health issues, identifying resources for addressing them, and developing and implementing community health improvement plans. MAPP consists of seven principles (Welter et al., 2021):

1. Systems thinking
2. Dialogue
3. Shared vision
4. Data to inform the process
5. Partnerships and collaboration
6. Strategic thinking
7. Celebration of successes

## ▶ CONCLUSION

This chapter focused on leadership and management in health education and promotion. We described some of the critical skills and strategies necessary to be an effective leader and to manage health education and promotion teams, including working with partners and stakeholders; assessing training needs and meeting these training needs; management of people and related human resources; management of budgets and acquiring additional funding resources; and conducting strategic planning of health education and promotion programs and community needs. In Chapter 9, we will touch on the Code of Ethics, which are essential principles that health education professionals and leaders must consider in all aspects of their leadership and management efforts in health education and promotion.

1. _____ involves an ongoing commitment to self-reflection and self-critique, power imbalances, and establishing and maintaining mutual benefits and equitable relationships.

   A. Cultural competence
   B. Cultural humility
   C. Cultural backgrounds
   D. Cultural beliefs

2. When deciding to delegate a task, which is the least important for a manager to do?

   A. Consider current workload
   B. Assess relevant skills
   C. Ensure it leads to a learning experience
   D. Evaluate the effect on morale

3. _____ reflects strategies and interventions to build skills of partners, stakeholders, and the organization.

   A. Leadership
   B. Negotiation
   C. Organizational development
   D. Teamwork

4. What portion of a budget should a health educator plan to spend for fringe benefits?

   A. 5% to 10%
   B. 15% to 20%
   C. 20% to 25%
   D. 25% to 30%

5. _____ involves cooperation or coordination of a group of individuals for a common purpose or goals.

   A. Leadership
   B. Goals
   C. Teamwork
   D. Management

### 1. B) Cultural humility

While there are any number of interpretations, Melanie Tervalon and Jann Murray-Garcia coined the term in 1989 and it criticaly contains the concepts of a) lifelong learning and critical self-reflection, b) recognizing and changing power imbalances, and c) institutional accountability.

### 2. C) Ensure it leads to a learning experience

Though it would be nice, not every task can be designed to be a learning experience. As a manager, it is more important to ensure that work is being done well and is distributed fairly and to look towards the morale of the staff.

### 3. C) Organizational development

Organizational development reflects the strategies and interventions aimed at building skills of partners, stakeholders, and the organization to ensure that personal and organizational goals can be achieved.

### 4. D) 25% to 30%

A good rule of thumb is to budget between one-quarter and one-third of the salary for fringe benefits.

### 5. C) Teamwork

Teamwork involves coordination and effective communication that aids in team-building and works to address common goals.

6. An organization has been awarded funds to develop a training kit to help public health nurses persuade vaccine-hesitant parents to catch their children up on recommended childhood vaccines. A progress report is due at the end of the year on the planned grant activities and the grant spending. Which of the following would be the first step in preparing the report for the funder?

A. Reviewing the stated requirements for the report
B. Gathering the available data
C. Drafting the report
D. Preparing and executive summary

7. _____ is a necessary part of organizational management which helps to establish priorities, common goals, use of resources, and planning for the team.

A. Strategic planning
B. Teamwork
C. An objective
D. Mission

8. Mobilizing for Action through Planning and Partnerships (MAPP) model includes which of the following principles?

A. Systems thinking
B. Partnerships and collaboration
C. A and B
D. None of the above

9. When hiring new employees, a health educator should never inquire about which of the following during the interview process?

A. The candidate's education and experience
B. Any challenges or difficulties the candidate has experienced in the past
C. The candidate's childcare arrangements
D. The learning style the candidate prefers

10. Checking references when hiring a job candidate is critical because it allows you:

A. To be sure you have hired the right person
B. To understand how they functioned in their past employment, educational, or volunteer experience
C. To tell if their last workplace environment is comparable to yours
D. To avoid confirming the candidate's academic credentials

11. Before approving a strategic plan, it is important to receive feedback and acceptance from whom?

A. The organization's management and staff
B. Key stakeholders
C. A and B
D. All related social service organizations in the area

## 6. A) Reviewing the stated requirements for the report

The first step is to review what the funder has required for the report. Many funders have specific requirements for their reports in content and/or structure. Before beginning a report, you must know what you are supposed to be reporting.

## 7. A) Strategic planning

Strategic planning involves a phase of planning and reviewing values, mission and vision, and goals and objectives to ensure partners, stakeholders, and the organization can work to develop a plan, including a timeline, for achieving health education and promotion program-related and organizational goals.

## 8. C) A and B

The principles of MAPP include systems thinking, dialogue, shared vision, data to inform the process, partnerships and collaboration, strategic thinking, and celebration of success.

## 9. C) The candidate's childcare arrangements

Areas of federal law and some state laws prohibit discriminating against employees due to their status as parents or caregivers. Interviewers must avoid asking direct questions about whether candidates have children, their ages, and what childcare arrangements are in place.

## 10. B) To understand how they functioned in their past employment, educational, or volunteer experience

Contacting references can give you, as the potential future employer, a sense of how the candidate functioned in their past work, educational, or volunteer environment. However, those environments may dramatically differ from your organization's and certainly cannot guarantee that this candidate is the right person for the job. It is also best practice to verify with the candidate's educational or credentialing organization that they hold the degrees/certifications they claim to—many organizations skip this step, so you cannot take it for granted that their last workplace did so.

## 11. C) A and B

While it might be nice to receive feedback from all related social service organizations in the area, it is likely unrealistic to think time and resources will permit it. However, at a minimum, feedback should be obtained from the organization's management and staff and key stakeholders.

12. Which of the following U.S. federal laws prohibits sharing most individually identifiable health information without prior authorization from an individual?

   A. National Labor Relations Act
   B. Americans With Disabilities Act
   C. Health Insurance Portability and Accountability Act (HIPAA)
   D. Occupational Safety and Health Act

13. An organization needs volunteers to help staff in a health clinic in an underserved area. What would be the first step in planning a recruitment campaign?

   A. Develop a website where volunteers could log their hours
   B. Schedule training for new volunteers
   C. Create job descriptions for the volunteer positions
   D. Use social media to help identify interested volunteers

14. Which of the following is the least helpful function of a program budget?

   A. Planning
   B. Monitoring
   C. Motivating
   D. Decision-making

15. The food bank and the healthcare clinics have developed a document indicating their common interests in serving the health of the people of the community and their willingness to provide referrals to each other's organizations. The document does not specify things more specific than that. That document can best be described as a:

   A. Memorandum of Understanding (MOU)
   B. Memorandum of Agreement
   C. Memorandum of Collaboration
   D. Memorandum of Cooperation

16. The food bank and the community-based Diabetes Prevention Program (DPP) have developed a document specifying that the food bank will refer clients to the community-based DPP for a certain fee per client. The document also has specific provisions for data sharing and specifies an end date. That document can best be described as a:

   A. Memorandum of Understanding
   B. Memorandum of Agreement
   C. Memorandum of Collaboration
   D. Memorandum of Cooperation

17. A health educator working in a large city plans to offer nutritional programming at several local, federally qualified health clinics aimed at helping those with complex medical needs eat a recommended diet. One barrier to implementing the plan is the lack of staff to lead the classes. What would be a logical next step for the health educator to take?

   A. Abandon the plan as unrealistic
   B. Charge people attending the clinics the cost of the classes, including staff
   C. Reach out to local universities to find student interns from dietitian programs
   D. Use lay volunteers to teach the classes

## 12. C) Health Insurance Portability and Accountability Act (HIPAA)

The HIPAA of 1996 prohibits sharing most individually identifiable information. However, there are exceptions, including those for public health protections, such as reportable diseases.

## 13. C) Create job descriptions for the volunteer positions

The first step would be to determine what tasks could be filled by volunteers and write the job descriptions for the volunteer positions. Until you know what you need people to do, you cannot offer training or advertise the positions on social media (or anywhere else). Developing a website for tracking hours may or may not be appropriate, given project resources, volunteer preferences, and job requirements.

## 14. C) Motivating

Budgets are helpful for planning, monitoring, and making decisions about program activities.

## 15. A) Memorandum of Understanding (MOU)

A MOU is a broad document indicating common interests and intended actions, but it is not specific or legally enforceable.

## 16. B) Memorandum of Agreement

A Memorandum of Agreement is a document specifying work on a specific project that has been agreed upon and outlining the terms and responsibilities of each partner.

## 17. C) Reach out to local universities to find student interns from dietitian programs

Using student interns would be a way to provide staff to lead classes who have technical knowledge but who would likely not add substantial costs to a program.

18. A health educator is asked to sit on a panel conducting reviews of funding proposals for community block grants. Which of the following is the health educator least likely to consider when making their recommendation on whether to fund a particular proposal?

    A. The volunteer training plan
    B. The research aims
    C. The budget justification
    D. The letters of support

19. A local health department is receiving calls expressing concern about the opening of a needle exchange facility in a neighborhood that has been beset with high rates of hepatitis C caused by the sharing of needles. The needle exchange facility is needed to reduce the exposure of injection drug users to infectious diseases, but the community's concerns need to be addressed. Which of the following methods would be the most effective and realistic way of gathering concerns from the community and exploring mutually agreeable solutions?

    A. Conduct random digit dialing telephone interviews with community residents
    B. Go door to door in the neighborhoods to interview people about their concerns
    C. Mail surveys to homes in the neighborhood
    D. With community partners, hold community meetings about the proposed facility

20. Which of the following is the least important to include when posting a job description?

    A. Job title
    B. Summary of responsibilities
    C. Educational requirements
    D. Number of vacation days

(See answers next page.)

## 18. B) The research aims
Research aims, budget justification, and letters of support are critical to most, if not all, funding proposals.

## 19. D) With community partners, hold community meetings about the proposed facility
Holding face-to-face community meetings in conjunction with community partners would be the most financially and time-efficient method of hearing community concerns while being able to explore potential solutions.

## 20. D) Number of vacation days
Typically, the number of vacation days is a negotiated benefit.

# ● REFERENCES

Greene-Moton, E., & Minkler, M. (2020). Cultural competence or cultural humility? Moving beyond the debate. *Health Promotion Practice, 21*(1), 142–145. https://doi.org/10.1177/15 24839919884912

Joly, B. M., Coronado, F., Bickford, B. C., Leider, J. P., Alford, A., McKeever, J., & Harper, E. (2018). A review of public health training needs assessment approaches: Opportunities to move forward. *Journal of Public Health Management and Practice: JPHMP, 24*(6), 571. https://doi.org/10.1097/PHH.0000000000000774

Koplan, J. P., Milstein, R. L., & Wetterhall, S. (1999). *Framework for program evaluation in public health*. U. S. Department of Health & Human Services.

Lockyer, J. (1998). Needs assessment: Lessons learned. *Journal of Continuing Education in the Health Professions, 18*(3), 190–192. https://doi.org/10.1002/chp.1340180310

Orton, S., Umble, K. E., Rosen, B., McIver, J., & Menkens, A. J. (2006). Management Academy for Public Health: Program design and critical success factors. *Journal of Public Health Management and Practice, 12*(5), 409–418. https://doi.org/10.1097/00124784-200609000-00002

Rowitz, L. (2014). *Public health leadership: Putting principles into practice*. Jones & Bartlett Publishers.

Welter, C. R., Jarpe-Ratner, E., Seweryn, S., Bonney, T., & Verma, P. (2021). Results from a national mixed-methods study exploring community health improvement implementation: An opportunity to strengthen public health systems through collective action. *Journal of Public Health Management And Practice: JPHMP, 28*, E653–E661. https://doi.org/10.1097/PHH.0000000000001459

Wright, K., Hann, N., McLeroy, K. R., Steckler, A., Matulionis, R. M., Auld, M. E., Brick, L., & Weber, D. L. (2003). Health education leadership development: A conceptual model and competency framework. *Health Promotion Practice, 4*(3), 293–302. https://doi.org/10.1177/1524839903004003014

Wright, K., Rowitz, L., Merkle, A., Reid, W. M., Robinson, G., Herzog, B., Weber, D., Carmichael, D., & Baker, E. (2000). Competency development in public health leadership. *American Journal of Public Health, 90*(8), 1202. https://doi.org/10.2105/AJPH.90.8.1202

# Area of Responsibility VIII: Ethics and Professionalism[1]

## ▶ INTRODUCTION

This chapter, and the final competency, covers two different but related topics concerning health education: ethics and professionalism. In some ways, it is the "everything else" chapter of information that has not been covered up to this point. (As a matter of fact, one of the competencies in this Area is "promote the health education profession to stakeholders, the public, and others," but we already covered the history of the Certified Health Education Specialist (CHES®) credential in Chapter 1, and we will address the information about professional development and opportunities for career advancement in Chapter 11, where we think it is actually a better fit.)[2] Nonetheless, these are skills and concepts that are crucial. The public health field in general is grappling with many ethical questions, from those looking at historic wrongs (such as research carried out without informed consent or adequate compensation) to modern-day ethical questions brought on by pandemics, climate change, or technological advancements.

## ▶ ETHICS

Health educators work with diverse audiences and populations. To help ensure that the actions of health educators are of the highest ethical standards, those who are certified as health educators by National Commission for Health Education Credentialing (NCHEC) must adhere to the guidelines set forth in the Coalition of National Health Education Organizations' *Code of Ethics for the Health Education Profession* (Exhibit 9.1). The Code is frequently updated (the earliest version first appeared in 1976).

Exhibit 9.1 *Code of Ethics for the Health Education Profession*

Preamble
The Code of Ethics provides a framework of shared values within Health Education professions. The Code of Ethics is grounded in fundamental ethical principles, including: value of life, promoting justice, ensuring beneficence, and avoiding harm. A Health Education Specialist's responsibility is to aspire to the highest possible standards of conduct and to encourage the ethical behavior of all those with whom they work.

Health Education professionals are dedicated to excellence in the practice of promoting individual, family, group, organizational, school, community, public, and population health. Guided

*(continued)*

---

[1] The Eight Areas of Responsibility for Health Education Specialists are copyright of the National Commission for Health Education Credentialing, Inc. (NCHEC).

[2] Competency 8.3 Engage in professional development to maintain and/or enhance proficiency (covered in Chapter 10); Competency 8.4 Promote the health education profession to stakeholders, the public, and others is covered in Chapter 12, copyright of the National Commission for Health Education Credentialing, Inc. (NCHEC).

**Exhibit 9.1** *Code of Ethics for the Health Education Profession* (*continued*)

by common goals to improve the human condition, Health Education Specialists are responsible for upholding the integrity and ethics of the profession as they perform their work and face the daily challenges of making ethical decisions. Health Education Specialists value equity in society and embrace a multiplicity of approaches in their work to support the worth, dignity, potential, quality of life, and uniqueness of all people.

Health Education Specialists promote and abide by these guidelines when making professional decisions, regardless of job title, professional affiliation, work setting, or populations served.

## Article I: Core Ethical Expectations

1. Health Education Specialists display personal behaviors that represent the ethical conduct principles of honesty, autonomy, beneficence, respect, and justice. The Health Education Specialist should, under no circumstances, engage in derogatory language, violence, bigotry, racism, harassment, inappropriate sexual activities or communications in person or through the use of technology and other means.
2. Health Education Specialists respect and support the rights of individuals and communities to make informed decisions about their health, as long as such decisions pose no risk to the health of others.
3. Health Education Specialists are truthful about their qualifications and the qualifications of others whom they recommend. Health Education Specialists know their scope of practice and the limitations of their education, expertise, and experience in providing services consistent with their respective levels of professional competence, including certifications and licensures.
4. Health Education Specialists are ethically bound to respect the privacy, confidentiality, and dignity of individuals and organizations. They respect the rights of others to hold diverse values, attitudes, and opinions. Health Education Specialists have a responsibility to engage in supportive relationships that are free of exploitation in all professional settings (e.g., with clients, patients, community members, students, supervisees, employees, and research participants).
5. Health Education Specialists openly communicate to colleagues, employers, and professional organizations when they suspect unethical practices that violate the profession's Code of Ethics.
6. Health Education Specialists are conscious of and responsive to social, racial, faith-based, and cultural diversity when assessing needs and assets, planning, and implementing programs, conducting evaluations, and engaging in research to protect individuals, groups, society, and the environment from harm.
7. Health Education Specialists should disclose conflicts of interest in professional practice, research, evaluation, and the dissemination process.

## Article II: Ethical Practice Expectations

### Section 1: Responsibility to the Public

Health Education Specialists are responsible for educating, promoting, maintaining, and improving the health of individuals, families, groups, and communities. When a conflict of issue arises among individuals, groups, organizations, agencies, or institutions, Health Education Specialists must consider all issues and give priority to those that promote the health and well-being of individuals and the public, while respecting both the principles of individual autonomy, human rights, and equity as long as such decisions pose no risk to the health of others.

A: Health Education Specialists advocate and encourage actions and social policies that promote maximal health benefits and the elimination or minimization of preventable risks and health inequities for all affected parties.

(*continued*)

**Exhibit 9.1** *Code of Ethics for the Health Education Profession* (*continued*)

> B: Health Education Specialists contribute to the profession by redefining existing practices, developing new practices, and by sharing the outcomes of their work.
> C: Health Education Specialists actively involve individuals, groups, stakeholders, and communities in the entire educational process to maximize the understanding and personal responsibilities of those who may be affected.

> **Section 2: Responsibility to the Profession**
>
> Health Education Specialists are responsible for their professional behavior, the reputation of their profession, promotion of certification for those in the profession, and promotion of ethical conduct among their colleagues.
>
> A: Health Education Specialists recognize the boundaries of their professional competence and are accountable for their professional activities and actions.
> B: Health Education Specialists maintain, improve, and expand their professional competence through continued education, research, scholarship, membership, participation, leadership in professional organizations, and engagement in professional development.
> C: Health Education Specialists contribute to the profession by refining existing professional health-related practices, developing new practices, and by sharing the outcomes of their work.
> D: Health Education Specialists give recognition to others for their professional contributions and achievements.

> **Section 3: Responsibility to Employers**
>
> Health Education Specialists are responsible for their professional behavior in the workplace and for promoting ethical conduct among their colleagues and employers.
>
> A: Health Education Specialists apply current, evidence informed standards and theories when fulfilling their professional responsibilities.
> B: Health Education Specialists accurately represent and report service and program outcomes to employers.
> C: Health Education Specialists maintain competence in their areas of professional practice through continuing education on a regular basis to maintain their competence.

> **Section 4: Responsibility in the Delivery of Health Education/Promotion**
>
> Health Education Specialists deliver evidence informed practices with integrity. They respect the rights, dignity, confidentiality, inclusivity, and worth of all people by using strategies and methods tailored to the needs of diverse populations and communities.
>
> A: Health Education Specialists remain informed of the latest scientific information and advances in health education theory, research, and practice.
> B: Health Education Specialists support the development of professional standards grounded in theory, best practice guidelines, and data.

(*continued*)

**Exhibit 9.1** *Code of Ethics for the Health Education Profession* (*continued*)

    C: Health Education Specialists adhere to a rigorous and ethical evaluation of health education/promotion initiatives.

    D: Health Education Specialists promote healthy behaviors through informed choice and advocacy, and do not use coercion or intimidation.

    E: Health Education Specialists disclose potential benefits and harms of proposed services, strategies, and actions that affect individuals, organizations, and communities.

    F: Health Education Specialists actively collaborate with a variety of individuals and organizations, and demonstrate respect for the unique contributions provided by others.

    G: Health Education Specialists do not plagiarize.

### Section 5: Responsibility in Research and Evaluation

Through research and evaluation activities, Health Education Specialists contribute to the health of populations and the profession. When planning and conducting research or evaluation, Health Education Specialists abide by federal, state, and tribal laws and regulations; organizational and institutional policies; and professional standards and ethics.

    A: Health Education Specialists ensure that participation in research is voluntary and based upon the informed consent of participants. They follow research designs and protocols approved by relevant institutional review committees and/or boards.

    B: Health Education Specialists respect and protect the privacy, rights, and dignity of research participants and honor commitments made to those participants.

    C: Health Education Specialists treat all information obtained from participants as confidential, unless otherwise required by law, and inform research participants of the disclosure requirements and procedures.

    D: Health Education Specialists take credit, including authorship, only for work they have performed and give appropriate authorship, co-authorship, credit, or acknowledgment for the contributions of others.

    E: Health Education Specialists report the results of their research and evaluation objectively, accurately, and in a timely manner.

    F: Health Education Specialists promote and disseminate the results of their research through appropriate formats while fostering the translation of research into practice.

### Section 6: Responsibility in Professional Preparation and Continuing Education

Those involved in the professional preparation and training of Health Education students and continuing education for Health Education Specialists are obligated to provide a quality education that meets professional standards and benefits the individual, the profession, and the public.

    A: Health Education Specialists foster an inclusive educational environment free from all forms of discrimination, coercion, and harassment.

    B: Health Education Specialists engaged in the delivery of professional preparation and continuing education demonstrate careful planning; state clear and realistic expectations; present material that is scientifically accurate, developmentally appropriate and inclusive; conduct fair assessments; and provide reasonable and prompt feedback to learners.

    C: Health Education Specialists provide learners with objective and comprehensive guidance about professional development and career advancement.

    D: Health Education Specialists facilitate meaningful opportunities for the professional development and advancement of learners.

Copyright (c) 2020 by the CNHEO

(*continued*)

**Exhibit 9.1** *Code of Ethics for the Health Education Profession (continued)*

**Code of Ethics Taskforce Members:**

Christopher Ledingham, MPH, PhD (Co-Chair) Keely Rees, PhD, MCHES® (Co-Chair) Andrea L. Lowe, MPH, CPH Elisa "Beth" McNeill, PhD, CHES® Fran Anthony Meyer, PhD, CHES®
  Holly Turner Moses, PhD, MCHES®, FESG Larry Olsen, MAT, MPH, Dr. P.H., MCHES® Lori Paisley, BS, MA. Kerry J. Redican, MPH, PhD, CHES ® Jody Vogelzang, PhD, RDN, CHES®, FAND Gayle Walter, PhD, CHES®

We strongly recommend that you review and become familiar with the Code of Ethics before you take the exam AND throughout your professional life. It is inevitable that conflict, decisions, and even misunderstandings will arise while developing, delivering, and evaluating health education across a variety of people and populations; the Code of Ethics provides guidance to "promote wellness and quality of living though principles of self-determination and freedom of choice."

The history of ethics in research in public health is the subject of much study. One of the most widely known, the Belmont Report, was published in 1978. The Belmont Report arose partly in response to atrocities committed during the Tuskegee Syphilis Studies and outlined procedures for the protection of human subjects during research studies. The three essential tenets are (Adashi et al., 2018):

1.  Respect for person: There shall be protections for the autonomy of all people and they shall be treated with courtesy, and participants shall give (and may revoke) informed consent. Researchers must be truthful and not deceive participants, with some potential exceptions under strict oversight by an institutional review board (IRB).
2.  Beneficence: "Do no harm"—research must maximize benefits and minimize risks to participants.
3.  Justice: Research must be fair and nonexploitative, with costs and benefits justly distributed across peoples and society.

With the publication of the Belmont Report, **IRBs** became mandated to review federally funded research protocols to ensure that research was being conducted in an appropriate manner. In practice today, many organizations and institutions have IRBs that review a range of research and intervention projects, regardless of the funding source.

Since the publication of the Belmont Report, other concepts have become germane to the conversation around ethics. Not all concepts apply to all situations, but it is helpful to have a working knowledge of the domains. A few others include:

- Criticality: those with the most need would benefit the most
- Equity: distributing resources to address disparities (see more on health equity below)
- Egalitarianism: the concept that all people are of equal value, and that interventions/ policies should minimize disparities
- Transparency: providing full and accurate information to all involved about how decisions are made
- Utilitarianism: the concept of the greatest good for the greatest number of people

Ethics are not a compartmentalized topic with health education despite the fact that they ARE artificially compartmentalized in an Area of Responsibility and this chapter! Instead, they should permeate every aspect of the work we do as health educators—from needs assessment through planning, implementation, evaluation, advocacy, communication, research, program management, training, consulting, and so on.

# ▶ HEALTH EQUITY

One of the overarching goals of Healthy People 2030 is "Eliminate health disparities, achieve health equity, and attain health literacy to improve the health and well-being of all." We have discussed health literacy in Chapter 7, but what exactly are health disparities and health equity? They are both terms that are used frequently by health educators, but they have distinct, if related, meanings.

The Centers for Disease Control and Prevention (CDC; 2022) defines **health disparities** as: "preventable differences in the burden of disease, injury, violence, or in opportunities to achieve optimal health experienced by socially disadvantaged racial, ethnic, and other population groups, and communities." Disparities can be present across a wide range of categories including, but not limited to:

- Race/ethnicity
- Gender
- Sexual orientation
- Age
- Religion
- Socioeconomic status
- Education level
- Disability status

The CDC (2022) defines **health equity** as: "when every person has the opportunity to 'attain his or her full health potential' and no one is 'disadvantaged from achieving this potential because of social position or other socially determined circumstances.'" They further note that inequities in health are reflected in differences in:

- Life spans
- Quality of life
- Rates of disease
- Disability
- Severity of disease
- Availability of and access to treatment
- Death

A third, critical concept in this domain is the social determinants of health (SDOH). Healthy People 2030 defines SDOH as "the conditions in the environments where people are born, live, learn, work, play, worship, and age that affect a wide range of health, functioning, and quality-of-life outcomes and risks."

SDOH greatly affect your health, well-being, and quality of life. Examples of SDOH include:

- Safe (or lack thereof) housing, transportation, and neighborhoods
- Racism, discrimination, and violence
- Education, job opportunities, and income
- Access to nutritious foods and physical activity opportunities
- Access to healthcare
- Air and water quality
- Language and literacy skills

You can see how SDOH can also contribute to health disparities. If you grow up in an area with poor housing, you are more likely to be exposed to lead in childhood and suffer the effects of lead poisoning, which can have lifelong effects. People with little access to grocery stores are less likely to have good nutrition, raising their risk of heart disease, diabetes, and obesity.

Health educators have a role to play in reducing health disparities and promoting health equity, often by helping to address SDOH. In particular, health educators can help to address issues such as health literacy, identifying and implementing appropriate evidence-based programs, advocating for needed changes, and ensuring appropriate evaluations are in place to capture lessons learned, identify unintended consequences, and move lessons learned forward.

## CULTURAL COMPETENCE

Cultural competence—what does that even mean? Scholars and experts do not agree on how to create culturally competent programs, and even a definition is hard to come by. Triandis (1995) defines **culture** as a group-level, shared set of normative beliefs, behaviors, norms, roles, values, and assumptions. We all exist within many cultures—our racial or ethnic culture; the culture of our region, state, or hometown; the culture of our work; our school; our neighborhood; our friends; our religion; and our place of worship. Books have been written on cultural competency relevant to health education.

One of the earliest definitions identifies cultural and linguistic competency as a set of congruent behaviors, knowledge, attitudes, and policies that come together in a system, organization, or among professionals that enables effective work in cross-cultural situations. A related concept, cultural respect, allows for the delivery of services that are respectful of and responsive to the health beliefs, practices, and cultural and linguistic needs of diverse patients or clients. As time has gone on, the concept has evolved to include not only individual level, but organizational levels of cultural competency, as well as the notion that cultural competency is not a set of skills but rather an attitude or approach to how culture can affect health services and health outcomes.

Principles of cultural competence include:

1. Define culture broadly.
2. Value clients' cultural beliefs.
3. Recognize complexity in language interpretation.
4. Facilitate learning between providers and communities.
5. Involve the community in defining and addressing service needs.
6. Collaborate with other agencies.
7. Professionalize staff hiring and training.
8. Institutionalize cultural competence.
   —Centers for Disease Control and Prevention National Prevention Information Network (2021)

While navigating the waters of cultural competency can be tricky, let us remember why it is important to keep culture in mind. Race, gender, ethnicity, country/region of origin, religious affiliation, and education level, among others, all contribute to health disparities. Providing care, including health education, to people with diverse values, beliefs, and behaviors is critical to narrowing the gaps in health status. Benefits of building an organization's cultural competence are:

- Increased respect and mutual understanding among those involved
- Increased creativity in problem-solving through new perspectives, ideas, and strategies

- Decreased unwanted surprises that might slow progress
- Increased participation and involvement of other cultural groups
- Increased trust and cooperation
- Reduction in the fear of mistakes, competition, or conflict (For instance, by understanding and accepting many cultures, everyone is more likely to feel more comfortable in general and less likely to feel the urge to look over their shoulders to be sure they are being "appropriate" in majority terms.)
- Promotion of inclusion and equality
     —University of Kansas Community Tool Box (n.d.)

Culture affects nearly everything people encounter in their daily lives—including how people communicate, comprehend, and respond to health information. Having culturally and linguistically competent health professionals can contribute to health literacy. Part of cultural competence is the ability of health organizations and practitioners to recognize the cultural beliefs, values, attitudes, traditions, language preferences, and health practices of diverse populations, and to apply that knowledge to help produce positive health outcomes.

It is crucial to recognize that health education professionals have our own culture and language, and these affect how we communicate with the public. Words like "incidence" and "prevalence" seem normal to us, as do the reasons we use them. Recognize that this information, and much more, may not be accessible—or accepted—by everyone.

For many individuals with limited English proficiency (LEP), the inability to communicate in English is a crucial barrier to accessing health information and services. Health information for people with LEP needs to be communicated plainly in their primary language, using words and examples that make the information understandable. Finding and employing interpreters who can communicate in culturally competent ways with people with LEP is a sensitive and important task, as is producing materials for people with LEP in their language of choice. Not only do the same "plain language" rules apply, but we must remember that people may or may not be literate in their preferred language. The way we think about health, illness, mental illness, nutrition, and so on may not be the way other cultures approach the same issues. To be truly culturally competent (if such a thing is even possible) requires a thorough understanding of not only the audience, but also of our own cultural perspectives and assumptions. It is a task of a lifetime—one that a health educator must understand can never be fully achieved.

### Further Reading

Center for the Application of Prevention Technologies, Substance Abuse and Mental Health Services Administration. (2016). *Cultural competence.* www.samhsa.gov/capt/applying-strategic-prevention/cultural-competence

Office of Communication and Public Liaison, National Institutes of Health. (2017). *Cultural respect.* www.nih.gov/institutes-nih/nih-office -director/office-communications-public-liaison/clear-communication/ cultural-respect

# APPLY RELEVANT THEORIES OF BEHAVIOR CHANGE AND MODELS OF IMPLEMENTATION

*There is nothing so practical as good theory.—Kurt Lewin.* Dr. Lewin's famous words are as relevant today as they were when he uttered them in the 1940s. Without a firm understanding of their audience and how human behavior changes, health educators are doomed to randomly try different interventions with no specific insight into how they might be successful. This section reviews several relevant behavioral and organizational change theories. A fuller review of such theories can be found in Appendix B of the National Cancer Institute's (2002) *Making Health Communication Programs Work: A Planner's Guide* ("The Pink Book") and Chapter 2 of the Institute of Medicine's *Speaking of Health: Assessing Communication Strategies for Diverse Populations* (2002).

## INDIVIDUAL-LEVEL THEORIES

### Health Belief Model

The Health Belief Model (HBM) was developed to help understand why people choose not to participate in programs to prevent or detect disease. The core constructs of the HBM are:

- **Perceived susceptibility**—The perception of the individual of how at risk they are of developing a particular condition.
- **Perceived severity**—The perception of the individual of how severe or serious the consequences would be of developing a particular condition.
- **Perceived benefits**—The individual's beliefs of how effective or beneficial certain actions (e.g., screenings, preventative behavior) would be at reducing a particular health threat.
- **Perceived barriers**—The individual's perception of conditions, actions, or consequences that might prevent them from taking the proposed preventive action (e.g., cost, pain, fear, time).
- **Cues to action**—Environmental or individual factors that encourage the preventive behavior.
- **Self-efficacy**—The individual's perceived ability to perform the behavior. This is a more recent addition to HBM that was included to expand the applicability of HBM into more long-term, complex behaviors, such as chronic-disease prevention and lifestyle-change programs.

#### Further Reading

Champion, V. L., Skinner, C. S., & Tiro, J. (2015). The health belief model. In K. Glanz, B. K. Rimer, & K. Viswanath. (Eds.), *Health behavior and health education: Theory, research, and practice* (5th ed.). Jossey-Bass.

### Theory of Reasoned Action/Theory of Planned Behavior

The Integrated Behavioral Model comes out of the long history of the Theory of Reasoned Action/Theory of Planned Behavior (TRA/TPB). The TRA/TPB posited that behavioral intention, that is, a person's intention to perform a particular behavior and their perceived control over that behavior, were the most important predictors of whether an individual would actually perform a behavior. The TRA contained four basic constructs:

- **Behavioral beliefs**—The beliefs a person has toward the outcome of performing a particular behavior.
- **Evaluations of behavioral outcomes**—The weight a person gives to what the likely outcome a behavior will have.

These first two constructs combine to create an individual's attitude toward a behavior. People with strong beliefs that a behavior will benefit them will have a positive attitude toward the behavior.

- **Normative beliefs**—How an individual perceives that people they care about perceive the behavior.
- **Motivation to comply**—How motivated a person is by their normative beliefs.

These last two constructs combine to form one's subjective norms.
The TPB, updated in the 1980s and 1990s added two additional constructs:

- **Control beliefs**—Positive and negative factors to allow the behavior to be performed.
- **Perceived power**—How important those facilitators or barriers are to the behavior.

### Further Reading

Montaño, D. E., & Kasprzyk, D. (2015). Theory of reasoned action, theory of planned behavior, and the integrated behavioral model. In K. Glanz, B. K. Rimer, & K. Viswanath. (Eds.), *Health behavior and health education: Theory, research, and practice* (5th ed.). Jossey-Bass.

## Transtheoretical Model

The Transtheoretical Model (TTM) posits that behavior change is a continually evolving process rather than a one-time event. An underlying assumption of the model is that individuals are at varying levels of motivation, or readiness to change, for each behavior at any one time. People at different stages of change need different interventions matched to where they are at a particular time. By knowing where an individual is, you can design appropriate and realistic interventions to move the individual farther along the continuum of behavior change.

There are five stages of behavior change in the model:

1. **Precontemplation**—The person is not thinking about changing the behavior.
2. **Contemplation**—The person is aware of the need for behavior change and is considering changing the behavior.
3. **Preparation**—The person has decided to change the behavior and is preparing to do so.
4. **Action**—The person is actively changing the behavior.
5. **Maintenance**—The person has changed the behavior and is adopting it as the new normal.

While it is tempting to think of this process as linear and progressive, it is not. People enter and exit the model at different stages and often revert to an earlier stage, or "fail" at behavior change/maintenance, and start over again somewhere on the continuum.

*Further Reading*

Prochaska, J. O., Redding, C. A., & Evers, K. E. (2015). The transtheoretical model and stages of change. In K. Glanz, B. K. Rimer, & K. Viswanath. (Eds.), *Health behavior and health education: Theory, research, and practice* (5th ed.). Jossey-Bass.

Prochaska, J. O., & Velicer, W. F. (1997). The transtheoretical model of health behavior change. *American Journal of Health Promotion, 12*(1), 38–48. https://doi.org/10.4278/0890-1171-12.1.38

## INTERPERSONAL LEVEL THEORIES

### Social Cognitive Theory

Social Cognitive Theory (SCT) is the most cited interpersonal-level theory a health educator is likely to use. SCT operates on the idea that an individual's behavior is the result of ongoing interactions between their internal psychosocial traits and the external environment in which they operate—called **reciprocal determinism**. Perhaps the most widely used construct from SCT is self-efficacy—an individual's belief that he or she can carry out a particular behavior and overcome any barriers to performing the behavior. There are several additional constructs in the theory:

- Behavioral capability
- Expectations
- Expectancies
- Self-control
- Emotional coping responses

*Further Reading*

Boston University School of Public Health. (2019). *Social Cognitive Theory.* https://sphweb.bumc.bu.edu/otlt/mph-modules/sb/behavioralchangetheories/behavioralchangetheories5.html

## ORGANIZATIONAL/COMMUNITY LEVEL THEORIES

### Diffusion of Innovations Theory

Diffusion of Innovations Theory describes how products, ideas, and/or social practices or norms that are perceived as "new" spread throughout a population. Diffusion theory has been used to study the adoption of a wide range of technologies and behaviors, including health behaviors and programs.

According to the theory, for any given innovation, people's adoption of the behavior or technology can be categorized as one of the following:

1. Innovators (2.5%)
2. Early adaptors (13.5%)
3. Early majority (34%)
4. Late majority (34%)
5. Laggards (16%)

According to Diffusion of Innovations Theory, diffusion occurs through a five-step process through which people make decisions. The five stages are the following:

1. **Knowledge**—Person becomes aware of innovation.
2. **Persuasion**—Person becomes interested in learning more about the innovation.
3. **Decision**—Person decides to adopt or reject the innovation.
4. **Implementation**—If the decision is made to adopt, implementation (of varying degrees) occurs. Further information gathering may occur.
5. **Confirmation**—The person finalizes the decision to adopt, working through internal issues (cognitive dissonance) or social interactions to confirm the adoption was desirable.

### Further Reading

Rogers, E. M. (2003). *Diffusion of innovations* (5th ed.). Free Press of Glencoe.

## Stage Theory

Stage Theory is based on the idea that organizations move through a series of predictable stages as they change. This is helpful for understanding where organizations are in the change process, to be able to match activities to the organization's stage of change. In the 1940s, Lewin proposed three stages: Unfreeze, Change, and Refreeze.

Modern Stage Theory takes Lewin's work and combines it with Rogers' Diffusion of Innovations Theory (2003) to create four stages of organizational change:

1. Developing the awareness of a problem and possible solutions
2. Deciding to adopt a change or innovation
3. Implementing the change (including changing organizational structures/supports)
4. Institutionalizing the change and making it part of the organization's structure/activities

### Further Reading

Butterfoss, F. D., Kegler, M. C., & Francisco, V. T. (2008) Mobilizing organizations for health promotion: Theories of organizational change. In K. Glanz, F. M. Lewis, & B. K. Rimer (Eds.), *Health behavior and health education: Theory, research, and practice* (4th ed.). Jossey-Bass.

## ▶ CONSULTING[3]

Health educators may either act as or need to hire consultants. In this section, we discuss issues relative to both situations. Let us address being hired as a consultant first. Occasionally, an organization will hire a consultant if they need to address a problem or situation but do not have an employee with the knowledge or capacity to address the situation. For example, imagine a police department is interested in improving its response to mental and behavioral health issues by increasing referrals to social service and behavioral health and substance abuse treatment, but they do not want to hire someone full time to do that work. Instead, they could hire a consultant to advise them how best to train their officers to identify situations in which mental health and substance abuse issues are relevant and make appropriate referrals. This is referred to as external consulting, when a health educator provides information or guidance

---

[3] Serve as an authoritative resource on health education and promotion.

to an organization or company he or she does not normally work with. The relationship is considered to be formal if there is a written contract.

On the other hand, as a health educator, you may be in a situation where your organization is in need of hiring a consultant to provide you with temporary support on a project. When selecting a consultant, your organization may follow a process that looks something like the following:

1. Identify if and why a consultant might be necessary for your project.
2. Check to see if all internal resources have been exhausted.
3. Solicit bids.
4. Assess the bids based on various criteria including fees, availability, experience, references, and prior work with your organization.
5. Interview the top candidates.
6. Hire your top pick. Retain the names of other qualified consultants for use on future projects or in case the initial choice does not work out or does not accept the job. These names may also be potential hires for jobs in the future—it is not unusual for people to move in and out of regular employment and consultative work, so keep networking or maintaining informal relationships with people and organizations. You never know when it may be useful to your career or your organization!

## INCORPORATING AND ADAPTING EVIDENCE-BASED PROGRAMS

Many health educators will want to be familiar with sources of evidence-based programs, or programs that have been shown to be reliable and valid (at least for certain populations). Following are the examples of common places to find evidence-based programs:

- Compendium of Evidence-Based Interventions and Best Practices for HIV Prevention: (https://www.cdc.gov/hiv/research/interventionresearch/compendium/index.html)
- National Institute of Health Evidence Based Practices and Programs (https://prevention.nih.gov/research-priorities/dissemination-implementation/evidence-based-practices-programs)
- Healthy People 2020 Evidence-based Resources (https://health.gov/healthypeople/tools-action/browse-evidence-based-resources)
- Substance Abuse and Mental Health Services Administration's (SAMHSA) National Registry of Evidence-based Programs and Practices (https://www.samhsa.gov/resource-search/ebp)
- U.S. Preventive Services Task Force (https://www.uspreventiveservicestaskforce.org/uspstf/recommendation-topics)
- The Community Guide (https://www.thecommunityguide.org/resources)

Often evidence-based programs must be adapted in some way when implemented. Some common ways programs are adapted include:

- Procedural (timing, recruitment, delivery, staffing)
- Dosage (number and length of classes/sessions)
- Content (adding/removing content)
- Participants (targeting a different demographic)
- Cultural (changing to fit the needs of a different culture; Moore et al., 2013)

Such changes are often inevitable in the real world, but they can alter the effectiveness of the program if they are not carefully considered, or if they are done in a reactive way. The changes least likely to interfere with the expected (evidence-based) outcomes of the program are those considered in advance and selected to enhance the program, as opposed to ones that happen because of carelessness or lack of planning (poor fidelity). For example, if adapting a program to a different culture, doing so in a community-based, participatory way, with an advisory group, and, ideally, in consultation with the original program developers, is more likely to lead to expected outcomes. Conversely, delivering only half the content because the original program was slated for a 2-hour class and you only have a 1 hour class-time available is unlikely to yield the expected results. Remember, something being an evidence-based program is not a GUARANTEE of results!

## ▶ CONCLUSION

Ethics and professionalism should be the bedrock of your health education practice. Over your career, what is considered "ethical" and "professional" is likely to change as mores and societal expectations change, which is why it is critical to stay abreast of the changes through education and professional development, which we will cover in Chapter 11.

But for now, you have made it through all Eight Areas of Responsibility. Next, it is time to put your knowledge to the test by actually taking a (mock) test—in Chapter 10.

1. Which is NOT a part of a theory?

   A. Concepts
   B. Definitions
   C. Propositions
   D. Conclusions

2. In a research study, the requirement of "informed consent" has to do with which ethical principle?

   A. Universalism
   B. Beneficence
   C. Respect for individuals
   D. Do no harm

3. According to the transtheoretical model, as an individual moved from precontemplation into maintenance, the lessening of negative beliefs and increasing of positive beliefs about a behavior is best described as:

   A. Self-actualization
   B. Self-efficacy
   C. Decisional balance
   D. Perception of benefits

4. For employees who quit smoking last week, what would be the most effective strategy for supporting them in their cessation attempt?

   A. Sending them information on the harms done by tobacco to the body
   B. Sending them graphic videos of the harms that tobacco does to the body
   C. Sending them messages about how most of their fellow employees do not use tobacco
   D. Sending a congratulatory note for having made it through the first week

5. A participant in a program states, "As a woman who did not ever breastfeed, I am at higher risk for breast cancer." Which of the following constructs of the Health Belief Model does this statement best demonstrate?

   A. Perceived barrier
   B. Perceived susceptibility
   C. Self-efficacy
   D. Cue to action

### 1. D) Conclusions

"A theory is a set of interrelated concepts, definitions, and propositions that present a systematic view of events or situations by specifying relations among variables in order to explain and predict the events or situations" (Glanz et al., 2002, p. 25).

### 2. C) Respect for individuals

Informed consent falls under the respect for individuals/autonomy pillar of the principles for ethical research.

### 3. C) Decisional balance

Decisional balance is a key construct of the Transtheoretical Model (TTM). It reflects that, at the beginning, the person is not adopting the new behavior because they either do not know about it or the "cons" outweigh the "pros." As they learn more, the information they gain reduces the "cons" and increases the "pros," leading to a shift in attitude and behavior. By action, the "pros" outweigh the "cons."

### 4. D) Sending a congratulatory note for having made it through the first week

Conscious-raising information (like information or graphic videos) are used in the beginning of Transtheoretical Model (TTM) to move people from precontemplation to contemplation. Increasing people's perceptions of public support for the new behavior is a middle-stage approach. By the time a person is in action, we reinforce the new behavior in positive ways and help to manage stimuli that would lead to relapse in behaviors.

### 5. B) Perceived susceptibility

"Perceived susceptibility" is how likely a person thinks they are to be at risk from a particular health threat. "Perceived barriers" are those things which stand in the way of adopting the new behavior. Self-efficacy is the confidence in being able to overcome barriers and perform the new behavior. A cue to action is the stimulus that triggers the new behavior.

6. A health educator is implementing a pilot project where rapid response teams are available to go into communities that have been affected by gun violence and provide grief counseling and support. If the program shows positive outcomes, it will be expanded. To ensure fidelity to intervention and track lessons learned during the implementation, the health educator should develop a MOP, which stands for:

   A. Manual on Places
   B. Manual of Plans
   C. Manual of Procedures
   D. Manual of Priorities

7. The Theory of Planned Behavior is a theory of health behavior aimed at which of the following levels?

   A. Individual
   B. Community
   C. Organizational
   D. Population

8. Identifying theories of behavior change and best practice models allows you to:

   A. Eliminate the need to do research on the audience
   B. Predict the success of an intervention strategy with precision
   C. Narrow the cause of a health problem to a single theory or model to make it easier to conceptualize and plan an intervention
   D. Identify determinants that lead people to problem behaviors and develop programs that are more likely to be successful in influencing the behavior

9. All of the following are reasonable approaches to take when the demand for a project exceeds project resources, except:

   A. Screening or wait-listing participants on a preset criteria
   B. Referring those not selected for an intervention to community resources
   C. Selecting those most at need for the intervention
   D. Selecting only one demographic group to serve for convenience of data collection

10. A health educator at a worksite is developing a health risk assessment. He writes, "Are you planning on quitting smoking in the next 30 days?" Which theory of change is the health educator using?

   A. Theory of Planned Behavior
   B. Theory of Reasoned Action
   C. Transtheoretical Model
   D. Social Cognitive Theory

11. In what stage of change would a smoker be who was planning on quitting in the next 30 days?

   A. Precontemplation
   B. Contemplation
   C. Preparation
   D. Action

## 6. C) Manual of Procedures
A Manual of Procedures, or MOP, is a document that contains policies, roles and responsibilities, procedures, and protocols for an implementation.

## 7. A) Individual
The Theory of Planned Behavior is an individual-level theory.

## 8. D) Identify determinants that lead people to problem behaviors and develop programs that are more likely to be successful in influencing the behavior
Theories help to identify the causes of the problem behaviors and guide the development of interventions that will then successfully intervene in the behavior.

## 9. D) Selecting only one demographic group to serve for convenience of data collection
When project resources have to be rationed, care must be taken to do so in an ethical matter. Providing a wait list, community referrals, and prioritizing needs are all ethical approaches if done thoughtfully and considered a priori. Selecting one demographic group for the convenience of the organization when there is high community demand is likely unethical.

## 10. C) Transtheoretical Model
The Transtheoretical Model posits that people move through stages in their way toward behavior change.

## 11. C) Preparation
In the Stages of Change model, people who are preparing to take action within the next 30 days are considered to be in Preparation.

12. The objective, "By the end of this training, the participant will be able to filter a gallon of water and list five items to pack in an emergency kit," addresses:

    A. Knowledge and skills
    B. Attitudes and knowledge
    C. Skills and behavior
    D. Skills and attitudes

13. In the United States, what is the name of the organization often charged with reviewing research study or intervention designs?

    A. Intervention Design Review
    B. Institutional Review Board (IRB)
    C. Intervention Review Board
    D. Intervention Review Committee

14. A health education specialist encounters a client with his family in the local grocery store. While they are all talking, the educator asks the client how he is responding to his diabetes medication. The health educator has violated which of the following responsibilities of the Health Education Profession's *Code of Ethics*?

    A. Nonmaleficence
    B. Confidentiality
    C. Informed consent
    D. Autonomy

15. According to the Diffusion of Innovations Theory, which of the following groups of people are the second to adopt a behavior?

    A. Laggards
    B. Innovators
    C. Early adopters
    D. Early majority

16. A health educator has been hired by a school district to advise on the selection of an evidence-based curriculum. The school district has identified a curriculum that they would like to use for their high schools, but it was originally designed for middle school students. What should the health educator advise them would be the most problematic change to make when adapting this program to an older audience?

    A. Changing the font of the materials into something more appealing to older teens
    B. Changing the pictures to look like older teens
    C. Rewriting the instructions to align with school holidays
    D. Replacing the included activities with ones from a different program intended for high school students

*(See answers next page.)*

## 12. A) Knowledge and skills
Filtering a gallon of water is a skill, but being able to list five items is a knowledge-level domain.

## 13. B) Institutional Review Board
IRB can also be known as Independent Ethics Committees (IEC) or Ethical Review Boards (ERB) in the United States.

## 14. B) Confidentiality
Article 1 of the *Code of Ethics for the Health Education Profession* (2020) states that "Health Education Specialists are ethically bound to respect the privacy, confidentiality, and dignity of individuals and organizations."

## 15. C) Early Adopters
Innovators are the very first to adopt a behavior. Early adopters are next.

## 16. D) Replacing the included activities with ones from a different program intended for high school students
There is always some concern when adapting evidence-based curriculum to different audiences because they have been proven to work in a certain audience/space/time and are not guaranteed to do so elsewhere. However, generally, minor changes that make an intervention more tailored to a different, but somewhat similar, audience should not change the core of the program greatly. Changes to the heuristics of messages—such as fonts and pictures—and tailoring instructions or other programmatic components such as incentives or activities—as long as it is tested and monitored—should not present a seismic shift in the program. Changing the activities of a program, however, changes the whole nature of the program.

17. A health educator is working on a new initiative to reduce lead in drinking water. Which social determinants of health (SDOH) are they addressing?

   A. Neighborhood and Built Environment
   B. Economic Stability
   C. Education Access and Quality
   D. Social and Community Context

18. A person's health and quality of life are dependent on many factors, including "the conditions in the environments where people are born, live, learn, work, play, worship, and age." These conditions are known as:

   A. Socioeconomic status
   B. Ecological model
   C. Social determinants of health (SDOH)
   D. Health promotion

19. A health educator working in Miami is interested in improving their cultural competence. Which of the following would be the least helpful activity for them to undertake?

   A. Consider their own culture and biases
   B. Collect race, ethnicity, and language preference data from their community
   C. Memorize a list of commonly used words in Spanish
   D. Advocate for monthly staff trainings

20. All of the following characteristics of an intervention may pose barriers to the dissemination of evidence-based programs, except:

   A. Interventions that lack flexibility
   B. Interventions that account for user's needs and preferences
   C. Interventions that have a high degree of technical sophistication
   D. Interventions that have garnered limited organizational support

### 17. A) Neighborhood and Built Environment
Environmental Health falls under the "Neighborhood and Built Environment" section of the SDOH in Healthy People 2030 along with Housing, Transportation, and Violence Prevention, among others.

### 18. C) Social determinants of health (SDOH)
Healthy People 2030 defines SDOH as "the conditions in the environments where people are born, live, learn, work, play, worship, and age that affect a wide range of health, functioning, and quality-of-life outcomes and risks."

### 19. C) Memorize a list of Spanish words
While it might be helpful for the health educator to speak Spanish, depending on what population they work with, considering their own culture, understanding the preferences of the populations they work with, and advocating for organizational change through trainings are more likely to improve cultural competence.

### 20. B) Interventions that account for user's needs and preferences
Interventions that consider beneficiaries' needs and preferences are more likely to be successfully disseminated than ones that are not developed considering these aspects.

# REFERENCES

Adashi, E. Y., Walters, L. B., & Menikoff, J. A. The Belmont Report at 40: Reckoning with time. *American Journal of Public Health, 108*(10), 1345-1348. https://doi.org/10.2105/AJPH.2018.304580

Center for Community Health and Development (University of Kansas). (n.d.). *Community toolbox. Building culturally competent organizations.* https://ctb.ku.edu/en/table-of-contents/culture/cultural-competence/culturally-competent-organizations/main

Centers for Disease Control and Prevention National Prevention Information Network. (2021). *Cultural competence.* https://npin.cdc.gov/pages/cultural-competence#1

Centers for Disease Control and Prevention. (2022). *Health equity.* https://www.cdc.gov/chronicdisease/healthequity/index.htm

Glanz, K., Rimer, B. K., & Lewis, F. M. (Eds.). (2002). *Health behavior and health education* (3rd ed.). Jossey-Bass.

Institute of Medicine. (2002). *Speaking of health: Assessing health communication strategies for diverse populations.* National Academies Press. https://doi.org/10.17226/10018

Moore, J. E., Bumbarger, B. K., & Cooper, B. R. (2013). Examining adaptations of evidence-based programs in natural contexts. *Journal of Primary Prevention, 34,* 147–161. https://doi.org/10.1007/s10935-013-0303-6

National Cancer Institute. (2002). *Making health communication programs work: A planner's guide.* U.S. Department of Health and Human Services, Public Health Service, National Institutes of Health. https://www.cancer.gov/publications/health-communication/pink-book.pdf

Rogers, E. M. (2003). *Diffusion of innovations.* Free Press of Glencoe.

Triandis, H. C. (1995). *Individualism and collectivism.* Westview Press.

Univeristy of Kansas Community Tool Box. *9. Enhancing cultural competence.* https://ctb.ku.edu/en/enhancing-cultural-competence

# Sample CHES® Exam

In this chapter, there are 165 sample test questions from each of the Eight Areas of Responsibility[1] in the expected proportion of an actual exam. Answers with identification of related competency will follow the exam. In the CHES® exam, 150 of the questions will be counted toward your score and 15 of the questions will be trial questions for potential use in future exams; you will not, of course, know which are the "real" questions. Try taking the sample exam in this chapter in circumstances similar to the CHES® exam by timing yourself and completing it in one sitting. Can you do it in less than 3 hours?

1. A team of researchers conducts an investigation into whether small incentives can encourage older adults to stop smoking. They publish their findings in a peer-reviewed journal. A newspaper then runs an article about their published findings. Using this scenario, please answer the following questions:
   The journal article is a _____ source.

   A. Primary
   B. Secondary
   C. Tertiary
   D. Quaternary

2. The newspaper article is an example of a _____ source.

   A. Primary
   B. Secondary
   C. Tertiary
   D. Quaternary

3. A health educator that is interested in better understanding and prioritizing the health needs of a population may want to conduct this type of assessment.

   A. Capacity
   B. Asset-based
   C. Needs
   D. Outcomes

---

[1] The Eight Areas of Responsibility for Health Education Specialists are copyright of the National Commission for Health Education Credentialing, Inc. (NCHEC).

**4.** A logic model can:

   **A.** Show funding sources
   **B.** Identify expected outcomes
   **C.** Enumerate planned activities
   **D.** Change underlying assumptions

**5.** Phase 1 of PRECEDE–PROCEED includes all of the following except:

   **A.** Articulating the community's needs and desires
   **B.** Considering the community's problem-solving capacity
   **C.** Identifying strengths and resources
   **D.** Considering enabling factors

**6.** Which of the following is true of Figure 10.1?

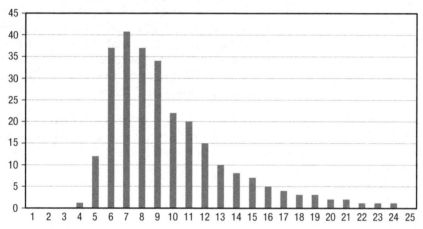

**Figure 10.1** Average number of self-reported servings of fruits and vegetables consumed per student at ABC School per week.

   **A.** Negatively skewed
   **B.** Positively skewed
   **C.** Symmetrical
   **D.** A and B

**7.** Common elements of a program proposal include an abstract, project plan, budget, and:

   **A.** Specific aims
   **B.** SMART aims
   **C.** Letters of support
   **D.** A and C

SCENARIO for QUESTIONS 8 and 9: A health educator is approached by a technology company about implementing its program, which uses tablets to deliver educational content to seniors in their homes to reduce social isolation and loneliness.

8. What would be the first question the health educator should consider before adopting the technology into the intervention?

   **A.** Is there funding available to offset the cost of the technology?

   **B.** How much training time will staff need to learn the technology?

   **C.** Will the technology be acceptable to or wanted by the population?

   **D.** Will the organization be perceived as innovative if it adopts the technology?

9. In this project, the app has provisions for those with loss of vision or hearing to enable them to participate in the program. Additionally, the program does not require seniors to leave their homes, so it is inclusive of those who have physical limitations that make travel difficult. These tablets are also being provided at little or no cost to low-income seniors. These accommodations are examples of what ethical principle?

   **A.** Beneficence

   **B.** Transparency

   **C.** Confidentiality

   **D.** Equity

10. A health educator is interested in understanding rates of childhood obesity in their community. They are utilizing data collected by federal, state, and local health departments, as well as data from their local hospitals and health organizations. What source of data is the health educator currently utilizing?

    **A.** Primary

    **B.** Secondary

    **C.** Tertiary

    **D.** Narrative

11. According to Bloom's Taxonomy, which classification of skills includes the ability to define, describe, label, or state?

    **A.** Comprehension

    **B.** Knowledge

    **C.** Application

    **D.** Evaluation

12. Jane Doe, PhD, Principal Investigator (effort = 3 calendar months). Dr. Doe will be responsible for the overall coordination and supervision of all aspects of the study, including hiring, training, and supervising staff/students; recruiting study participants; coordinating treatment and assessment components; scheduling and staff assignments; and data management. Additionally, she will conduct the training sessions, assist with statistical analysis, and be responsible for reporting the project's findings.

    This is an example of a:

    **A.** Job description

    **B.** Performance review

    **C.** Study plan

    **D.** Budget justification

13. Creating messages specifically aimed at an individual based on their particular characteristics is called:

    A. Cultural competency
    B. Drafting
    C. Tailoring
    D. Personalizing

14. The nonprofit professional organization that credentials health education professionals and students in both the United States and internationally is:

    A. CEPH
    B. SOPHE
    C. NCHEC
    D. SHAPE

15. A health educator tasked with reducing motor vehicle accidents discovers that federal funds have been made available to add bike lanes to major roads. These funds would be an example of what kind of factor?

    A. Predisposing
    B. Reinforcing
    C. Enabling
    D. Institutional

16. All of the following are strategies or plain language writing except:

    A. Using short sentences
    B. Using passive voice
    C. Using images or other media
    D. Using bullet points

17. This tool can help with program planning and evaluation by depicting the inputs, activities, outputs, and short- and long-term outcomes.

    A. Benchmarks
    B. Logic model
    C. Gantt chart
    D. Mission statements

18. Which of the following is the correct order of the PROCEED model for public health planning?

    A. Implementation, process evaluation, impact evaluation, outcome evaluation
    B. Implementation, impact evaluation, process evaluation, outcome evaluation
    C. Process evaluation, implementation, impact evaluation, outcome evaluation
    D. Formative evaluation, implementation, outcome evaluation, impact evaluation

19. A health education specialist encounters a client with his family in the local grocery store. While they are all talking, the educator asks the client how he is responding to his diabetes medication. The health educator has violated which of the following responsibilities of the Health Education Profession's *Code of Ethics*?

    **A.** Nonmaleficence
    **B.** Confidentiality
    **C.** Informed consent
    **D.** Autonomy

20. An important distinction between program evaluation and research is that evaluation:

    **A.** Is always more expensive
    **B.** Is not intended to be generalizable to a wider population
    **C.** Is easier to do
    **D.** Is more useful

21. Which one of the following is the correct rank for heart disease as a cause of mortality for individuals between the ages of 55 and 64, and for all individuals in total, in the United States, in 2020?

    **A.** First, first
    **B.** Second, first
    **C.** Third, second
    **D.** Third, first

22. Which one of the following interventions is the best example of primary prevention?

    **A.** Mammography
    **B.** Physical therapy
    **C.** Tracheostomy
    **D.** Immunization

SCENARIO for QUESTIONS 23 and 24: A heath education specialist is designing a program for residents in a low-income area. A needs assessment has shown those residents have lower-than-average rates of annual flu vaccination. The educator decides to hold a flu shot clinic, and residents who get a flu shot will be given $500.

23. This incentive could be called into question because it could be considered:

    **A.** Coercive
    **B.** Culturally insensitive
    **C.** Discriminatory
    **D.** Cost-effective

24. In this scenario, the educator would be violating which of the following responsibilities for health education practice?

    **A.** Financial
    **B.** Moral
    **C.** Legal
    **D.** Ethical

25. _____statistics make predictions about a population based on a sample of data taken from the population in question.

    A. Inferential
    B. Descriptive
    C. Experimental
    D. Applied

26. Logic models can be constructed:

    A. Right-to-left only
    B. Left-to-right or right-to-left
    C. Left-to-right only
    D. From the bottom up

27. Which of the following aims to find evidence of disease early to reduce morbidity and mortality?

    A. Primary prevention
    B. Secondary prevention
    C. Tertiary prevention
    D. Quaternary prevention

28. By December 31, 62 Senators will have voted for the "Support Public Health Funding Act" is an example of a:

    A. Program goal
    B. Behavioral objective
    C. Advocacy objective
    D. Communication objective

29. Voting registration drives and developing a press release in support of a bill are examples of:

    A. Advocacy strategies
    B. Grassroots advocacy only
    C. Media advocacy only
    D. Unethical behavior

30. The duration of the study, the potential risks and benefits, and the requirements of the study are all pieces of information necessary for:

    A. SMART objectives
    B. Record reviews
    C. The Belmont Report
    D. Informed consent

**31.** Periodic data collection to ensure that advocacy programs are being implemented as they were intended is called:

   **A.** Correlation study
   **B.** Outcome evaluation
   **C.** Fidelity monitoring
   **D.** Input monitoring

**32.** Which of the following is an example of a learning objective?

   **A.** The community nurse educator will demonstrate the correct use of a blood pressure cuff
   **B.** The group facilitator will explain two benefits of medication adherence
   **C.** The principals will participate in a trauma-informed teaching workshop
   **D.** The conference attendee will be able to demonstrate how to perform cardiopulmonary resuscitation (CPR)

**33.** Cochrane Reviews, The Community Guide, and Agency for Healthcare Research and Quality (AHRQ) Innovations Exchange are good sources of:

   **A.** Vital statistics
   **B.** Indexed literature reviews
   **C.** Evidence-based programs
   **D.** Funding

**34.** The Centers for Disease Control and Prevention (CDC) Evaluation Framework begins with:

   **A.** Engaging stakeholders
   **B.** Describing the program
   **C.** Gathering credible evidence
   **D.** Developing goals and objectives

**35.** A systematic application of audits, checks, and corrections to ensure that strategies and methods during program implementation are of the highest quality possible is also called:

   **A.** Quality assurance
   **B.** Delphi process
   **C.** Program evaluation
   **D.** Internal affairs

**36.** When designing health communication campaigns, which is the correct order to plan and implement a campaign?

   **A.** Assess needs, write goals/objectives, choose channel(s), implement, evaluate
   **B.** Write goals/objectives, assess needs, choose channel(s), implement, evaluate
   **C.** Assess needs, choose channel(s), write goals/objectives, implement, evaluate
   **D.** Choose channel(s), assess needs, write goals/objectives, implement, evaluate

**Refer to Figure 10.2 for questions 37 to 39.**

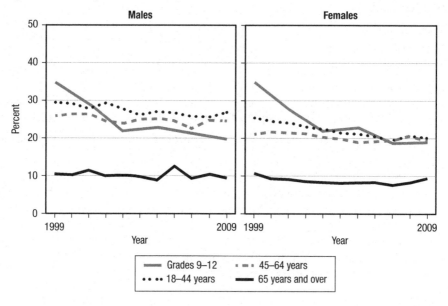

**Figure 10.2** Cigarette smoking among students in Grades 9 through 12 and adults age 18 and older, by sex, grade, and age, in the United States from 1999 through 2009.

37. According to Figure 10.2, in 2001, which of the following was true?

   **A.** The smoking rate for male children and adults aged 18 to 44 was essentially the same
   **B.** Seniors' rates of smoking increased dramatically over the previous year
   **C.** In the 45 to 64 age group, a higher percentage of women smoked when compared to men
   **D.** Rates of smoking in high school girls was at its highest point

38. According to Figure 10.2, during the period of 2005 to 2009, seniors experienced:

   **A.** Universally declining rates of smoking
   **B.** A brief uptick in smoking rates in males, followed by a return to baseline
   **C.** A sharp increase in smoking across the board
   **D.** The lowest rates of smoking recorded by women in 2009

39. According to Figure 10.2, who had the lowest rate of smoking in 2007?

   **A.** Men over the age of 65
   **B.** Women aged 18 to 44
   **C.** Women over the age of 65
   **D.** Men aged 18 to 44

40. When creating materials for grassroots lobbying efforts, SMOG, Flesch–Kincaid, and Gunning Fog are all examples of tools to assess:

    A. Cultural competence
    B. Policy briefs
    C. Reading level
    D. Kurtosis

41. "In the next 2 years, there will be a 30% increase in the number of new parents who say they intend to vaccinate their babies on time" is an example of a:

    A. Program goal
    B. Learning objective
    C. Educational objective
    D. Behavioral objective

42. _____ reflects a measurement tool's ability to measure a variable consistently and _____ reflects a measurement's tool to measure what it is supposed to measure.

    A. Reliability/validity
    B. Validity/reliability
    C. Validity/variation
    D. Variation/reliability

43. The type of evaluation that measures whether an advocacy campaign has resulted in the desired change is called:

    A. Monitoring
    B. Formative
    C. Process
    D. Outcome

44. Perceived severity, perceived susceptibility, and perceived benefits are all constructs in which theory or model?

    A. Theory of Reasoned Action
    B. Theory of Planned Behavior
    C. Transtheoretical Model
    D. Health Belief Model

45. A health educator is teaching a class on how to preserve food from a community garden through pressure canning. They want to make sure that the participants have correctly understood the procedure. Which of the following is a technique for assessing whether the participants learned the skill?

    A. Call back
    B. Teach back
    C. Scribner's method
    D. Call and response

**46.** Flip charts, models, audiovisual presentations, and movies are all examples of what kind of media a health educator might employ during advocacy work?

A. Interactive

B. Collaborative

C. Educational

D. Persuasive

**47.** A health education specialist is designing a social media campaign to increase breastfeeding initiation in young women of color. The best group to work with to design, pretest, and refine messages would be:

A. Pediatricians

B. High school teachers

C. Public health nurses

D. Young women of color

**48.** Cultural competency, the ability to navigate systems, and functional literacy are all components of:

A. Numeracy

B. Health literacy

C. SMOG

D. Cultural literacy

**49.** A food bank provides funding to local food vendors to enable them to provide fresh produce to residents in a food desert. Which of the following would be considered a medium-term outcome for this project?

A. Patrons purchase more fresh fruits and vegetables

B. The vendor tracks the number of fresh produce items offered

C. The rate of diabetes is reduced in the community

D. Participants say Tuesdays are the best days for the vendors to sell fresh produce

**50.** A legislator has become convinced of the need to take action on stabilizing the price of certain pharmaceutical prices. They direct their staff to begin drafting legislation on the matter. What Stage of Change are they in?

A. Precontemplation

B. Contemplation

C. Preparation

D. Action

**51.** Which of the following is true of communicating across cultures?

A. Cultural competence can be achieved through careful study and practice

B. A positive attitude and willingness to learn is sufficient

C. Self-reflection is necessary for developing better communication practices

D. Experiences living in other cultures are necessary for true understanding

**52.** One way that program monitoring differs from other kinds of evaluation efforts, such as outcome evaluation studies, is that program monitoring is:

  **A.** Optional
  **B.** Continuous throughout the program
  **C.** Quantitative
  **D.** Theory-driven

**53.** A health education specialist working at a university implements a campaign to reduce underage drinking. The campaign is focused on changing the perception that all college students binge drink on the weekend and instead communicating that most college students do not drink or drink moderately on the weekend. This campaign is based on which construct from Social Cognitive Theory?

  **A.** Social norms
  **B.** Self-efficacy
  **C.** Observational learning
  **D.** Situation

**54.** A broad, future-oriented statement reflecting an aspirational aim of a program or organization is called a:

  **A.** SMART objective
  **B.** Goal
  **C.** Mission statement
  **D.** Vision statement

**55.** In a logic model, "staff," "funding," and "a swimming pool" would be considered:

  **A.** Outcomes
  **B.** Activities
  **C.** Inputs
  **D.** Outputs

**56.** In a logic model, the creation of "swimming classes" and "a website for participants to log the number of hours they swim" would be a considered:

  **A.** Outcomes
  **B.** Assumptions
  **C.** Inputs
  **D.** Outputs

**57.** Which of the following is true about program goals and objectives?

  **A.** Program participants should have the final say in determining them
  **B.** They should be determined at the beginning of the planning process
  **C.** They may be altered to better fit evaluation data
  **D.** They can be better determined once implementation occurs

58. Which of the following is NOT a framework for program evaluation?

    A. Reach
    B. RE-AIM
    C. PRECEDE–PROCEED
    D. EBMR

59. A health educator needs to identify a nutritional training program for school staff who have had an influx of refugees into the school district. The school board has authorized funding for the training modality the health educator feels is most appropriate, so cost is not a limiting factor, but coordinating staff schedules has proved difficult. Which of the following options would be the best for the health educator to select?

    A. Two 2-hour long in-person trainings from a nutritionist specializing in traditional cuisines of the refugees
    B. A 1-hour asynchronous online module on developing a strengths-based approach to school–family relationships
    C. One 2-hour training session offered both in-person and online with a nutritionist and staff from a local relocation agency, to be offered twice over the course of a semester
    D. A 1-hour webinar with breakout rooms (synchronous discussion opportunities) about supporting staff and students through changing school environments

60. In developing a campaign to get men to see their primary care physicians for regular health screenings, you find that their wives are often the ones who make their husband's doctor appointments. You decide to speak to a local women's group on the importance of men's healthcare. In this case, which kind of audience are the women?

    A. Primary
    B. Secondary
    C. Tertiary
    D. Quaternary

61. When collecting primary data, which of the following survey methods is likely to be the most expensive?

    A. In-person interview
    B. Telephone-based survey
    C. Mail-based survey
    D. Social media–based survey

62. A woman is considering quitting smoking but is very sure that if she does so, she will gain weight. A health educator using the Theory of Planned Behavior would have to influence which construct to address this concern?

    A. Perceived behavioral control
    B. Subjective norm
    C. Behavioral intention
    D. Attitude

63. A program evaluator is concluding an evaluation of a program that assessed fall hazards in seniors' homes as part of a local meal delivery program. The program determined that there was a significant need for retrofitting bathrooms to improve safety. As they conclude the evaluation, what should be their last step in this project?

    A. Share the results at community meetings and with local stakeholders
    B. Write a report to the funder
    C. Describe the problem to the seniors
    D. Form a coalition

64. If a health problem is highly changeable and highly important to the population, which strategy should a health education specialist employ?

    A. Health education
    B. Social marketing
    C. Legal interventions
    D. Incentives

65. A _____ is a visual that helps to present all the tasks that need to be completed as part of program implementation, such as inputs, major activities, due dates, and outputs.

    A. Flow chart
    B. Dashboard
    C. Logic model
    D. Gantt chart

66. All of the following are important concepts in social marketing except:

    A. Consumer research
    B. Comprehensiveness
    C. Cost-effectiveness
    D. Competition

67. A health educator is hired to lobby Congress to raise taxes on junk food and use the revenue to lower the price of fruits and vegetables. Which form of communication would be most likely to gain the desired outcome?

    A. Face-to-face meetings
    B. Social media
    C. Letters
    D. Conference calls

68. A health education specialist who can identify, articulate, and translate an understanding of the mission, vision, values, beliefs, and ethics of an organization is exhibiting:

    A. Visionary leadership
    B. Sense of mission
    C. Understanding of political competencies
    D. Social dynamics

69. The following are all generally components of an operational budget except:

   A. Fixed costs
   B. Variable costs
   C. In-kind donations
   D. Revenue

70. A good data analysis and reporting plan will:

   A. Outline how the data for each monitoring and evaluation question will be coded
   B. Describe how conclusions will be justified, how stakeholders will be kept informed, and when activities will be implemented
   C. Plan for how monitoring and evaluation narratives will tell the same story
   D. A and B

SCENARIO for QUESTIONS 71 and 72: A review of vital records shows a worrisome uptick in fatal car accidents. Upon further research, it is revealed that a high proportion of fatal car crashes involve drivers playing a new type of game on their smartphone while driving. A needs assessment shows that most people have never considered the particular risk of this behavior, and news has not spread of the number of crashes it caused.

71. What would be the first intervention a health educator should try to reduce the number of people playing this new game while driving?

   A. Education
   B. Social marketing
   C. Fear campaign
   D. Legislation

72. What would be the type of intervention a health educator might advocate after a variety of educational and persuasive techniques showed little impact on lowering the number of drivers still playing the game, and causing car crashes?

   A. Education
   B. Social marketing
   C. Fear campaign
   D. Legislation

73. Which of the following questions would help a health educator who is assessing needs for a new policy?

   A. What are the campaign goals?
   B. How can multiple agencies work together to advocate for changes?
   C. What funding is available?
   D. Who is having this problem?

SCENARIO for QUESTIONS 74 and 75: A large rural school district has struggled with low vaccination rates due to parental resistance and preferences for "natural" treatments. Recently, an unvaccinated child returned from travel abroad and became sick with measles, leading to an outbreak in a local elementary school.

74. A group of parents started an online campaign encouraging other parents in the district to email or call the school board and their local representatives, asking them to enact strict requirements for vaccination to attend schools. The parent group's actions are an example of:

    A. Lobbying

    B. Media advocacy

    C. Electioneering

    D. Advocacy training

75. The parent group forms a nonprofit organization and hires a health educator to lead their advocacy efforts. The group is preparing to go to their state's legislature to speak to their representatives to request the state laws be changed to strengthen vaccine requirements for school. Which of the following is the most important thing for the health educator to include in the fact sheet they are preparing for the group to distribute at the State House?

    A. Scientific data tables from the Centers for Disease Control and Prevention (CDC) and National Institutes of Health (NIH) on the rise of measles nationally and internationally

    B. Quotes from teachers at the school

    C. The drop in standardized test scores following the outbreak

    D. Several pages of background and supporting evidence to facilitate decision-making

76. This type of data collection method involves conducting interviews with stakeholders who have specific expertise on a health topic or problem area of interest.

    A. Focus group

    B. Triangulation

    C. Key informant

    D. Nominal group

77. The "M" in SMART objective stands for:

    A. Manageable

    B. Measurable

    C. Maximizing

    D. Malleable

78. What are the "4 Ps" of social marketing?

    A. Planning, price, people, and products

    B. People, place, package, and produce

    C. Product, price, place, and promotion

    D. Planning, package, people, and price

79. According to the Diffusion of Innovations Theory, which of the following groups of people are the first to adopt a behavior?

    A. Laggards
    B. Early adopters
    C. Innovators
    D. Early majority

80. A student health program at a large university has hired a health educator to propose a health promotion program. The first thing the health educator should do is:

    A. Talk to students about their health concerns
    B. Develop goals and objectives to reduce drinking
    C. Use the Transtheoretical Model to stage student's readiness to change
    D. Develop evaluation metrics

81. _____ is the activity by which a person with specialized knowledge and skills is paid to help another person or organization make better decisions or plans.

    A. Consulting
    B. Training
    C. Teaching
    D. Researching

82. Perceived threat of a disease, perceived barriers, and cues to action are all constructs from which theory or model?

    A. Theory of Planned Behavior
    B. Theory of Reasoned Action
    C. Health Belief Model
    D. Ecological Model

83. In a SWOT (strengths, weaknesses, opportunities, and threats) analysis, opportunities, and threats are:

    A. Within your control
    B. Outside your control
    C. What your audience is doing
    D. What your partners are doing

84. This process involves identifying needs, setting priorities, examining causes of problems, determining and allocating resources, and exploring barriers to achieving objectives.

    A. Program planning
    B. Pilot testing
    C. Program implementation
    D. Program evaluation

85. Which of the following is the correct order of steps to take to develop a focus group?

    **A.** Determine the focus group questions to be asked> Determine the objectives of the focus group> Recruit participants> Determine a data analysis plan

    **B.** Determine the objectives of the focus group> Determine the focus group questions to be asked> Recruit participants> Determine a data analysis plan

    **C.** Determine the objectives of the focus group> Recruit participants> Determine the focus group questions to be asked> Determine a data analysis plan

    **D.** Determine the objectives of the focus group> Determine the focus group questions to be asked> Determine a data analysis plan> Recruit participants

86. Which of the following is NOT a limitation of survey data?

    **A.** Closed-ended questions may have lower validity

    **B.** Lack of context

    **C.** Geographical limitations

    **D.** Social-desirability bias

87. An owner of a medium-sized manufacturing plant is interested in beginning a worksite health promotion program. Which of the following is a true statement about using focus groups to develop a needs assessment?

    **A.** A focus group will give you highly generalizable data from which to base your program planning decisions

    **B.** Focus groups should consist of approximately eight to 10 employees and should be an assortment of management and labor to get a full understanding of employee opinions

    **C.** The final report of information gathered in focus groups should not be shared back to the participants to preserve confidentiality

    **D.** Even if you design, recruit, and analyze your focus groups well, you may need additional needs assessment information

88. Data that are sorted into categories (such as gender) are considered what type of data?

    **A.** Ratio

    **B.** Nominal

    **C.** Interval

    **D.** Rank order

89. Which of the following is a document that indicates shared interest and broadly lays out an intended common line of action, but is NOT legally binding?

    **A.** Memorandum of Agreement (MOA)

    **B.** Memorandum of Understanding (MOU)

    **C.** Cooperative agreement

    **D.** Partnership pledge

90. The social determinates of health include all but the following:

    **A.** Availability of resources

    **B.** Exposure to crime

    **C.** Quality schools

    **D.** Exposure to toxic substances

91. Lecture, brainstorming, coaching, debates, and role-playing are all examples of:

    A. Training simulations
    B. Teaching strategies
    C. Public speaking
    D. Peer review

92. A health educator plans a training to help parents of children diagnosed with rare diseases lobby for funding to research their children's conditions. The health educator would choose to employ a pretest–posttest evaluation strategy to assess which of the following from the training?

    A. Participant's satisfaction with the training
    B. Transferability of skills
    C. Change in knowledge
    D. Dollars raised for rare diseases by the parents

93. The first step in program planning is:

    A. Assessing existing health needs and problems
    B. Evaluating program objectives
    C. Analyzing a communication strategy
    D. Identifying populations

94. A_____ is typically concerned with monitoring fidelity in terms of program inputs, outputs, activities, and overall program implementation efforts.

    A. Process evaluation
    B. Formative evaluation
    C. Outcome evaluation
    D. Impact evaluation

95. The Hierarchy of Effects Model lists the steps through which behavior change happens in which order?

    A. Acquisition of skills, change in attitude, short-term retention of information, one-time performance of behavior, reinforcement of behavior, maintenance of behavior
    B. Change of attitude, acquisition of skills, short-term retention of information, long-term retention of information, decision-making, reinforcement of behavior, maintenance of behavior
    C. Change of attitude, acquisition of skills, decision-making, short-term retention of information, long-term retention of information, decision-making, reinforcement of behavior, maintenance of behavior
    D. Acquisition of skills, change in attitude, short-term retention of information, long-term retention of information, decision-making, reinforcement of behavior, maintenance of behavior

96. Which of the following is NOT a potential element of a quasi-experimental design?

    A. Comparison group
    B. Randomization
    C. Matching
    D. Participant selection bias

97. When planning a program for a local nonprofit, which of the following should be most important to a health education specialist?

A. A similar program's evaluation data
B. State health department goals and objectives
C. Needs assessment data
D. Behavioral Risk Factor Surveillance System (BRFSS) data

98. If a survey question measures what it is intended to measure, it is:

A. Reliable
B. Skewed
C. Valid
D. Accurate

99. Which of the following would NOT be a consideration for assessing whether an intervention caused an outcome?

A. Dose–response
B. Strength of association
C. Biologic plausibility
D. Correlation

100. The data collection approach that often yields the most helpful information to program planners while balancing efficiency and generalizability with the ability to explore needs of subgroups within a population is:

A. Quantitative
B. Qualitative
C. Mixed methods
D. Secondary

101. Effective health communication messages should be all of the following except:

A. Consistent
B. Clear
C. Credible
D. Capricious

102. A small nonprofit devoted to helping adults with mental disabilities live as independently as possible has decided to use volunteers to help drive program participants to work-training programs. Which of the following would be the most likely concern for using volunteer labor in this capacity?

A. The costs of training volunteers to transport participants in such a way as to satisfy liability concerns
B. The volunteers would know who was a participant in the program
C. Volunteers might get bored
D. Funders might not approve of using volunteers

103. An owner of a medium-sized manufacturing plant is interested in beginning a worksite health promotion program. Which of the following are likely to be of least interest to the owner when evaluating outcomes?

    A. Direct measures of productivity
    B. Time frame for the realization of benefits
    C. Employee leisure-time activities
    D. Health insurance costs

104. *Healthy People 2030* describes _____ as "the conditions and the environments where people are born, live, learn, work, play, worship, and age that affect a wide range of health, functioning, and quality of life outcomes and risks."

    A. Social determinates of health
    B. Ecological factors
    C. Allostatic load
    D. Public policy factors

105. Which of the following is an example of qualitative data?

    A. Vital statistics
    B. In-depth interviews
    C. Pretests and posttests
    D. Meta-analysis

106. The five broad categories, from most to least individual, common to the Social Ecological Model are:

    A. Innate, intrapersonal, interpersonal, institutional, federal, international
    B. Intrapersonal, interpersonal, neighborhood, organizational, state, federal
    C. Innate, intrapersonal, interpersonal, institutional, community, public policy
    D. Individual, workplaces, community, federal, international

107. The study design generally perceived as having the most convincing evidence that an intervention caused an outcome is:

    A. Case-control study
    B. Interrupted time series
    C. Direct observation
    D. Randomized control study

108. A community is addressing heart disease by implementing a number of new initiatives including: holding healthy eating and exercise classes, promoting community gardening groups, establishing farmers' markets that accept food stamps, and banning the use of trans-fatty acids in restaurant food. Which theory or model has likely influenced the development of this campaign?

    A. Health Belief Model
    B. Social Ecological Model
    C. Theory of Planned Behavior
    D. Stage Theory

109. Which of the following is the most important group of individuals to have advising a health educator interested in reducing drunk driving in the Midwest?

    A. State legislators and their staff
    B. Young men who have been convicted of driving under the influence (DUI)
    C. Pastors, rabbis, and other clergy from local houses of worship
    D. Police

110. The Social Ecological Model assumes that health and well-being are affected by _____ of multiple determinates including biology, behavior, the environment, and policy.

    A. Linkages
    B. Connections
    C. Communications
    D. Interactions

111. A health educator needs to recruit new volunteers for a grassroots advocacy program. Which of the following techniques is likely to be the most effective?

    A. Extending personal invitations through program staff, stakeholders, or clients
    B. Finding those required to do community service
    C. Social media advertising
    D. Recruiting the volunteers from similar organizations

112. _____ uses principles such as audience segmentation and cost-effectiveness to plan, implement, and evaluate how health education programs can bring about behavioral change.

    A. Social media
    B. Health marketing
    C. Health communication
    D. Social marketing

113. Data collected by a researcher for the sake of informing a specific project is called:

    A. Tertiary
    B. Primary
    C. Secondary
    D. Generalizable

114. A health educator has been hired to lead a community group through a strategic planning process. What would be an appropriate first step to take?

    A. Conduct an environmental assessment
    B. Convene a steering committee
    C. Develop mission/vision statements and indirect costs
    D. Set goals and objectives

115. Addressing a participant in communication materials by name, and including details specific to that individual's knowledge, attitudes, and preferences, is an example of what kind of health communication?

   A. Mass
   B. Social
   C. Tailored
   D. Specific

116. Preparing for a large-scale health education campaign—including conducting formative research, developing and testing materials, and preparing for implementation—takes approximately how long?

   A. 1 month
   B. 3 months
   C. 6 months
   D. 12 months

117. Process indicators measure:

   A. The program's activities and outputs
   B. Whether the program is achieving the expected effect
   C. Whether there has been a change in health status
   D. How cost-effective the program was

118. A community coalition is drafting a press release about a naloxone distribution event they will be holding in conjunction with a rally to encourage the local town council to open a safe injection clinic. Their press release should contain the following except:

   A. A spokesperson's name and contact information
   B. Second-person language
   C. Quotes from a leader in the organization
   D. The organization's boilerplate

119. During the assessment phase of advocacy work, a health educator discovers a regular meeting of a group of individuals representing diverse community organizations to collaboratively address a common goal. This group can best be described as a:

   A. Strategic planning committee
   B. Coalition
   C. Community-based program
   D. Community advisory committee

120. The first thing a health educator should do when beginning a needs assessment is:

   A. Conduct a community analysis
   B. Assess reinforcing factors
   C. Understand the health literacy levels of the community
   D. Determine project budget

**121.** _____ is providing direct, specific feedback and advice to an organization about developing and/or implementing a program with the express purpose of building capacity, improving skills, and transferring knowledge and experience.

    **A.** Technical assistance

    **B.** Mentoring

    **C.** Collaborative learning

    **D.** Contracting

**122.** All of the following would be good techniques for a face-to-face meeting with a legislator except:

    **A.** Have a specific, tailored message

    **B.** Make sure everyone in the group speaks

    **C.** Make an appointment

    **D.** Leave a fact sheet

**123.** Good examples of secondary data include all of the following except:

    **A.** Vital records

    **B.** Behavioral Risk Factor Surveillance System (BRFSS)

    **C.** Interviews

    **D.** Bureau of Labor Statistics

**124.** A _____ study involves a group of people from whom data are collected prospectively or can be gleaned from historical record.

    **A.** Time-series

    **B.** Case-control

    **C.** Experimental

    **D.** Cohort

**125.** Approximately what percentage of Americans have low health literacy?

    **A.** 20%

    **B.** 30%

    **C.** 40%

    **D.** 50%

**126.** Sources of qualitative data include all of the following except:

    **A.** Participant observation

    **B.** Focus groups

    **C.** Diary reviews

    **D.** Behavioral Risk Factor Surveillance System (BRFSS)

127. A health educator is asked to write a literature review for a grant proposal his organization is submitting to develop a project to test local schools for environmental contaminants. Which one of the following should he NOT do in the literature review portion of the proposal?

    A. Build an argument for the program
    B. Demonstrate the relevance of the program
    C. Present epidemiologic data related to the issue under study
    D. Describe how they will measure variables in program

128. When communicating health information to a reluctant audience, an instructor would find which of the following to be the least important?

    A. Emphasize the instructor's education and experience
    B. Explain why the topic is important
    C. Explain the value of acquiring the new knowledge or skills
    D. Engage the learner through multiple teaching styles

129. A health educator is asked to present findings from a community needs assessment to a local church. Which would be the first thing he should do to prepare an effective presentation?

    A. Use presentation software
    B. Find out more about the audience
    C. Visit the space where he will be presenting
    D. Write learning objectives

130. A _____ is defined as a "statement that *defines* the expected goal of a curriculum, course, lesson or activity in terms of demonstrable skills or knowledge that will be acquired by a student as a result of instruction."

    A. Learning objective
    B. Behavioral objective
    C. SMART objective
    D. Program objective

131. A _____ is a trial run of a program in order to evaluate feasibility, time, cost, acceptability, and potential adverse events.

    A. Prelaunch
    B. Pretest
    C. Pilot project
    D. Fidelity test

132. An example of _____ would be starting a petition to request that speedbumps be installed to slow traffic while an example of _____ is contacting a member of Congress to solicit funds for a traffic study.

    A. Electioneering/direct advocacy
    B. Grassroots advocacy/direct advocacy
    C. Indirect advocacy/direct advocacy
    D. Electioneering/grassroots advocacy

133. According to Bloom's Taxonomy, which of the following verbs shows the highest level of skills?

    A. List
    B. Use
    C. Justify
    D. Analyze

134. How does a theory differ from a model or framework?

    A. A theory is more likely to be tested and proven by research
    B. A model is more helpful for understanding a health problem
    C. Theories are specific to a setting or context
    D. Theories guide the identification, development, and implementation of health education programs or interventions

135. The three main kinds of indicators program evaluation seeks to understand are:

    A. Contributing, direct, indirect
    B. Process, outcome, impact
    C. Simple, precise, measurable
    D. Specific, measurable, achievable

136. Someone who is learning new information is most likely to remember it when they have:

    A. Read it
    B. Seen it
    C. Heard about it and seen it
    D. Done it and taught it to someone else

137. The last step in a community needs assessment should be:

    A. Analyzing data gathered
    B. Creating SMART objectives
    C. Sharing and validating the needs that have been identified
    D. Obtaining Behavioral Risk Factor Surveillance System (BRFSS) data

138. A health educator wants to ensure that the materials and services at their environmental health organization is offering are culturally appropriate for their Latinx audience. What would be a good first step for the health educator to take?

    A. Hire a translator to translate all written materials into Spanish
    B. Create a community advisory board to inform organizational activities
    C. Develop a policy to require more minorities to be interviewed for client-facing positions
    D. Fund a study to better understand their audience's exposure to environmental hazards

139. When assessing the quality of online information, which of the following is the least important to ask?

   A. Who is responsible for this site?
   B. Is the information evidence based?
   C. Is the information up-to-date?
   D. Is the information written in an active or passive voice?

140. Which of the following best describes a Delphi panel process?

   A. A group of four to 10 homogeneous people discussing a potential change
   B. The use of structured questionnaires used to generate consensus in a group of experts
   C. A small group of people privately ranking available possibilities to decide which should be prioritized
   D. A statistical analysis of separate but similar data in order to determine statistical significance

141. Adults with low health literacy levels are most likely to get their health information from which sources?

   A. Newspapers
   B. TV
   C. Facebook
   D. B and C

142. A _____ allows health educators to get feedback from participants about program materials.

   A. Pilot test
   B. Pretest
   C. Pilot project
   D. Posttest

143. Which age group has the highest percentage of people who use the internet regularly?

   A. 18 to 29
   B. 30 to 49
   C. 50 to 64
   D. 65+

144. A health educator has planned an intervention that will ensure that families in a high-risk area for infant death have safe sleeping areas for their babies. She plans to visit homes where babies are expected to make sure they have cribs set up and the environment is safe. She is concerned that parents may be resistant to having her come into their homes, despite having been told in several focus groups with pregnant mothers from the community that they would be interested in such a program and developing relationships with several community gatekeepers. What should she do before launching the program?

   A. Hold more focus groups
   B. Do a literature search to get more information on safe sleep
   C. Launch a pilot project in one neighborhood
   D. Focus on something else

145. The Epidemiological Model for needs assessment asks all of the following questions except:

    A. Who had the problem?
    B. What is the problem?
    C. What will solve the problem?
    D. Why do those with the problem have it?

146. Common sources of secondary data include all of the following except:

    A. MMWR
    B. BRFSS
    C. NHANES
    D. CINAHL

147. A school board is selecting a sexual health education curriculum to implement in ninth grade. Which is the least important issue for them to gather data about?

    A. Cost
    B. If students will be embarrassed by the curriculum
    C. If parents support the curriculum
    D. Feedback of other school districts about the competing curriculum

148. All of the following are techniques to help promote learning except:

    A. Facilitate discussions rather than just lecture
    B. Avoid repetition
    C. Move from simple to complex ideas
    D. Explain to the learners why the information is important

149. A health educator is working on a project investigating childhood asthma in a public school system in a metropolitan school district. After obtaining institutional review board (IRB) and parental approval, she randomly samples students from across the school district and asks them questions about their asthma and treatment. She finds that among those who have been diagnosed with asthma, 70% do not have their asthma medication available to them at all times during the day at school. This type of study is:

    A. Time series
    B. Case control
    C. Ecological
    D. Cross-sectional

150. In a school district that has struggled with low vaccination rates due to parental resistance and preferences for "natural" treatments, an unvaccinated child becomes sick with the measles. The school board decides to hire a health educator to launch a campaign to promote vaccinations for school-aged children. This is an example of:

    A. A teachable moment
    B. Coercive behavior
    C. Incentives
    D. A pilot study

151. A _____ is defined as a "statement of what students ought to be able to do as a consequence of instruction."

    **A.** Behavioral objective
    **B.** Attitudinal objective
    **C.** SMART objective
    **D.** Program objective

152. _____ validity is concerned with the degree to which findings of your research or program evaluation outcomes are generalizable to other groups, settings, or contexts.

    **A.** External
    **B.** Primary
    **C.** Secondary
    **D.** Internal

153. When using presentation software, it is considered a best practice to:

    **A.** Use a lot of animations to keep the audience interested
    **B.** Practice the presentation before presenting it in public
    **C.** Limit the text on the slides to only the most important concepts
    **D.** B and C

154. A health educator is interested in understanding what health services are needed by employees in a certain company. Which of the following audiences would be least helpful to consult?

    **A.** Employees
    **B.** Management
    **C.** Former employees
    **D.** Human resources department

155. Descriptive study designs include all of the following except:

    **A.** Cross-sectional
    **B.** Case control
    **C.** Cohort
    **D.** Pretest–posttest design

156. A workplace installs high-efficiency particulate absorbing (HEPA) filters and monitors the $CO_2$ levels in an effort to control respiratory viruses in the winter. This is an example of what kind of intervention?

    **A.** Community based
    **B.** Policy change
    **C.** Behavior change
    **D.** Environmental

157. A state senator proposes offering parents in a low-income area a $1,000 savings account for college if their child is fully vaccinated (or medically exempt) upon enrollment in elementary school. A coalition of child health advocates, including several health educators, express concern about the incentive because it could be:

    A. Irrelevant
    B. Biased
    C. Discriminatory
    D. Coercive

158. A health education specialist working in an OB/GYN clinic in an under-resourced area has been tasked with developing a brochure for expectant mothers, explaining to them the importance of being screened for several infectious diseases during pregnancy. Many of the mothers did not graduate high school. The best approach for developing such a brochure would be to:

    A. Download a brochure from the state health department for expectant mothers on screening in pregnancy
    B. Create a brochure based on the health educator's experience with the topic
    C. Draft a brochure and then get feedback from patients at the clinic
    D. Draft a brochure and ask a doctor at the clinic to review it

159. Which of the following are the least likely for a health educator to be able to influence in a community?

    A. Biologic factors such as genetics
    B. Psychosocial factors such as public acceptance for people with disabilities
    C. Environmental factors such as lead in drinking water
    D. Behavioral factors such as increasing vegetable consumption

160. Low health literacy is associated with which outcomes?

    A. Better communication with clinicians
    B. Overuse of emergency department services
    C. Lower risk of adverse outcomes
    D. Increased medication compliance

161. A health educator is asked to address the topic of obesity in a senior care center. Many of the seniors receive food stamps and have limited health literacy skills. The health educator believes that it is critical to use a variety of methods to help address the problem. Which of the following are essential to the success of the health educator's program?

    A. An e-learning facility
    B. Adequate funding
    C. Dance classes
    D. A and B

162. By far, the greatest number of Americans speak English or Spanish. What are the three next most commonly spoken languages, in order of their frequency of use?

    A. Chinese, French, Tagalog
    B. French, Chinese, Vietnamese
    C. Arabic, Vietnamese, French
    D. Tagalog, French, Arabic

163. Health education specialists are often responsible for developing and implementating this type of plan that targets audiences, promotes messages, and uses a range of communication methods.

    A. Implementation plan
    B. Marketing plan
    C. Data collection plan
    D. Evaluation plan

164. Where is the error in this logic model (Figure 10.3)?

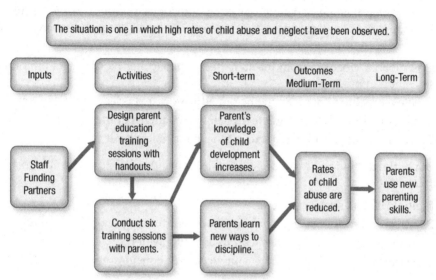

**Figure 10.3.** Logic Model for a situation in which high rates of child abuse and neglect have been observed

    A. The inputs are actually outputs
    B. The activities are not achievable
    C. The short-term outcomes are not theory-based
    D. The medium and long-term outcomes are not plausible

165. When searching for health information online, the most important issue for a health educator to consider for each website is:

    A. Whether the site has attractive colors and pictures
    B. If the website has a search feature
    C. If all sources are cited using the American Psychological Association (APA) style
    D. The relevance of the information to the intended audience

# Sample CHES® Exam Answers With Rationales

When you check your answers, is there one or more Areas of Responsibility you feel you need to review? Remember, we strongly encourage you to use other materials in addition to this guide to help you review!

1. **A) Primary (Area I)**
   Primary sources are those containing original research or data. Secondary sources such as newspaper or magazine articles synthesize or report on primary source material.

2. **B) Secondary (Area I)**
   Secondary data is data or a source that was collected by someone else. The newspaper article was written ABOUT the research, making it a secondary source.

3. **C) Needs**
   A needs assessment helps the health educator identify, analyze, and prioritize the needs of a priority population.

4. **D) Change underlying assumptions (Area V)**
   A logic model can and should identify underlying assumptions, but it cannot change them.

5. **D) Considering enabling factors (Area II)**
   Phase 1 of PRECEDE–PROCEED is the Social Diagnosis Phase. Enabling factors are considered in Phase 3.

6. **B) Positively skewed (Area IV)**
   Negatively skewed graphs have tails to the left. Positively skewed graphs have tails to the right.

7. **D) A and C (Area VII)**
   Program proposals often contain specific aims, which set the scope of the project and include letters of support from organizations that will be involved with the program.

8. **C) Will the technology be acceptable to or wanted by the population? (Area VII)**
   The first questions must be "Does the population want this technology?" and "Is it acceptable to them?" Only after those questions are answered can other questions be asked.

9. **D) Equity (Area V)**
By not only considering whether physical disabilities will prevent use, but by actually using technology to overcome physical limitations, as well as ensuring that financial resources are not a barrier, the ethical principle of equity is being upheld.

10. **B) Secondary (Area I)**
Secondary data involves data collected by others that may include federal, state, and local health departments, federally qualified health centers, hospitals, and other health organizations. For instance, a health educator might use data on obesity for the region from the Centers for Disease Control and Prevention (CDC) as part of *The Morbidity and Mortality Weekly Report (MMWR)*.

11. **B) Knowledge (Area VI)**
Knowledge (or Remembering) is the lowest level in Bloom's Taxonomy.

12. **D) Budget justification (Area VII)**
Budget justifications describe proposed costs for a project. Generally, they explain staffing and supply costs in sufficient detail for a reviewer to understand the necessity for each proposed cost within the project.

13. **C) Tailoring (Area III)**
Tailored messages are custom fitted to an individual, or groups of individuals, based upon particular characteristics they hold. These frequently include stage of change, demographic factors, or health condition or behavior.

14. **B) SOPHE (Area VIII)**
SOPHE, or the Society for Public Health Education, was founded in 1950.

15. **C) Enabling (Area II)**
Enabling factors are those factors in the environment that facilitate action and any skills or resources that are required to perform specific behavior. These can include resources such as funding.

16. **B) Using passive voice (Area VI)**
Messages should be written in active voice. When using an active voice, the subject acts upon its verb. For example: The health educator teaches youth about healthy eating (Active) versus the youth were taught about healthy eating by the health educator (Passive).

17. **B) Logic model (Area II)**
A logic model is a flowchart that depicts the key elements of a program including resources, inputs, activities, outputs, objectives, and short-term, intermediate, and long-term outcomes.

18. **A) Implementation, process evaluation, impact evaluation, outcome evaluation (Area II)**
The four phases of the PROCEED Model are implementation, process evaluation, impact evaluation, outcome evaluation.

19. **B) Confidentiality (Area VIII)**
Article 1, Section 4 of the *Code of Ethics for the Health Education Profession* states that "Health Educators are ethically bound to respect the privacy, confidentiality, and dignity of individuals."

20. **B) Is not intended to be generalizable to a wider population (Area IV)**
Program evaluation is intended to judge the merit or worth of a particular program, not to produce generalizable knowledge.

21. **B) Second, first (Area I)**
In 2020, cancer killed 110,243 adults between the ages of 55 and 64 and heart disease killed 696,692 Americans in total (80% of them over the age of 65), making it the number one cause of death (Centers for Disease Control and Prevention [CDC]; wisqars.cdc.gov/data/explore-data/home).

22. **D) Immunization (Area II)**
Primary preventions, like immunizations, seek to prevent disease. Secondary preventions seek to detect diseases early so they can be treated before they become more serious.

23. **A) Coercive (Area VIII)**
A very high value incentive ($500) could be considered coercive because people could be persuaded into taking the vaccination simply to receive the incentive. This is particularly true given that the intervention is taking place in a low-income area.

24. **D) Ethical (Area VIII)**
Coercive incentives are a violation of Article II, Section IV of the *Code of Ethics for The Health Education Profession*.

25. **A) Inferential (Area IV)**
**Inferential statistics** makes inferences about a population based on a sample of data taken from the population.

26. **B) Left-to-right or right-to-left (Area IV)**
When constructing a logic model from the left, the resources available lead to activities, and the activities to the outcomes (sometimes referred to as an "if . . . then" construction). When constructing logic models right-to-left, the desired outcomes drive the necessary activities, and the activities necessitate the resources (commonly referred to as the "but how?" construction).

27. **B) Secondary prevention (Area II)**
Secondary prevention, such as mammography, uses screening techniques to identify disease early to reduce morbidity and mortality.

28. **C) Advocacy objective (Area V)**
SMART objectives are helpful when planning and evaluating advocacy work.

29. **A) Advocacy strategies (Area V)**
Advocacy techniques can include encouraging potential voters to register and electioneering, or actively taking part in the activities of a particular candidate's campaign.

30. **D) Informed consent (Area VIII)**
   Informed consent is the means by which researchers provide information to potential participants on the potential risks and benefits of being involved in a research study. The specifics of informed consent will be dictated by an institutional review board (IRB), but would include the duration, risks and benefits, and requirements of the study.

31. **C) Fidelity monitoring (Area V)**
   Fidelity monitoring ensures that any program—advocacy or otherwise—is implemented as it was intended.

32. **D) The conference attendee will be able to demonstrate how to perform cardiopulmonary resuscitation (CPR) (Area II)**
   Learning objectives should be student-centered, use action verbs (ideally from Bloom's Taxonomy), and should break down the task to focus on specific, measurable, cognitive, or skill-based processes.

33. **C) Evidence-based programs (Area VIII)**
   These, as well as others such as Substance Abuse and Mental Health Services Administration (SAMSHA)'s Guide to Evidence-Based Practices, are sources of evidence-based practices or interventions that have been proven through study to work.

34. **A) Engaging stakeholders (Area IV)**
   The steps in the CDC Evaluation Framework are: (a) engage stakeholders, (b) describe program, (c) focus evaluation design, (d) gather credible evidence, (e) justify conclusions, and (f) use and share lessons learned. www.cdc.gov/eval/framework/index.htm

35. **A) Quality assurance (Area III)**
   Merriam-Webster defines quality assurance as "a program for the systematic monitoring and evaluation of the various aspects of a project, service, or facility to ensure that standards of quality are being met."

36. **A) Assess needs, write goals/objectives, choose channel(s), implement, evaluate (Area VI)**
   First you must define the problem, set goals/objectives, develop your intervention (including choosing your channels), implement your plan, and then evaluate to see how it went. See www.cdc.gov/healthcommunication/healthbasics/HowToDo.html for more information.

37. **A) The smoking rate for male children and adults aged 18 to 44 was essentially the same (Area I)**
   Looking at Figure 10.2, in 2001, the rates of smoking for males in grades 9 through 12 and males aged 18 to 44 are nearly the same, making this the best answer.

38. **B) A brief uptick in smoking rates in males, followed by a return to baseline (Area I)**
   The figure shows that males had a brief increase in smoking in 2006, which returned to around 10% for the remaining years. Female seniors' rates remained under 10% for the period.

39. **C) Women over the age of 65 (Area I)**
   Female seniors' rates remained under 10% for the period.

40. **C) Reading level (Area V)**
These are all tools you use when assessing reading level for health literacy work.

41. **D) Behavioral objective (Area II)**
The main difference between goals and objectives is their specificity. Goals are more general and include words such as "increase, decrease, raise, lower" but without specifics. Here, the targets and time frame identify this as an objective. The objective is targeting a behavior rather than a knowledge, making it a behavioral objective rather than a learning objective.

42. **A) Reliability/validity (Area IV)**
Reliability refers to the repeatability of findings. If the study were to be done a second, third, or fourth time, would it yield the same results? If so, the data are reliable. Validity refers to the credibility of the research.

43. **D) Outcome (Area IV)**
Outcome, or summative (some say impact) evaluation, seeks to understand whether there was a change in the population in some manner. In advocacy work, that generally results in a policy change or the rejection of a policy change.

44. **D) Health Belief Model (Area VIII)**
People can be influenced by the perceived severity, susceptibility, benefits (or threats) of a particular behavior or health condition, according to the Health Belief Model.

45. **B) Teach back (Area VI)**
Utilizing the teach back method can be very effective for making sure your audience understood what they were being taught. This technique may be especially useful when teaching those with low levels of health literacy who cannot rely on written instructions. See https://www.ahrq.gov/health-literacy/improve/precautions/tool5.html

46. **C) Educational (Area V)**
Educational media is designed to supplement instruction by highlighting main points and aiding the audience in retaining information.

47. **D) Young women of color (Area VII)**
The primary audience is nearly always the best source of information for the development and design of messages. Secondary audiences, such as teachers, nurses, and pediatricians, might be valuable sources of information, but the young women would be the true experts on what would be the best social media messages to write.

48. **B) Health literacy (Area VI)**
Health literacy is dependent on individual and systemic factors including: communication skills of lay persons and professionals, lay and professional knowledge of health topics, culture, demands of the healthcare and public health systems, and the demands of the situation/context.

49. **A) Patrons purchase more fresh fruits and vegetables (Area VI)**
Determining the best days to sell produce would be an example of a formative evaluation outcome. The vendor tracking the number of produce items offered is a process outcome. Rates of diabetes would be an example of a long-term outcome. Produce consumption, which could influence diabetes rates, is a medium-term outcome.

50. **C) Preparation (Area V)**
The Preparation stage of the Transtheoretical Model encompasses people who are preparing to enact the behavior change—in this case, introducing the legislations.

51. **C) Self-reflection is necessary for developing better communication practices (Area VI)**
Self-reflection and examination is a key cornerstone of cultural humility and cross-cultural communication best practices. To communicate well, we must understand our own culture, biases, philosophies, and approaches to health or whatever topics we are communicating.

52. **B) Continuous throughout the program (Area IV)**
Program monitoring should be ongoing throughout the implementation of a program. It is the method by which evaluations ensure that program activities are being implemented according to the program plan and that problems are addressed in a timely, ethical, and systematic way. It is not optional, and may contain qualitative, quantitative, or mixed methods.

53. **C) Observational learning (Area VIII)**
By offering credible role models who display the targeted behavior, you are demonstrating observational learning or modeling, which is a construct in the Social Cognitive Theory.

54. **D) Vision statement (Area II)**
Vision statements tend to be more aspirational and forward looking while mission statements are more concrete and focus on what the organization currently does. Vision can be thought of as "where we are going" and mission is "how we are going to get there."

55. **C) Inputs (Area III)**
In a logic model, inputs are the resources you need to conduct a program.

56. **D) Outputs (Area III)**
In a logic model, outputs are the activities or products produced by the program. In this case, classes, or a website would be activities or products created by a program, thus outputs.

57. **B) They should be determined at the beginning of the planning process (Area II)**
Program goals and objectives should be determined at the beginning of the planning process to guide the development of the plan. Without goals and objectives, a health educator would not have anything to guide the development of the project.

58. **D) EBMR (Area IV)**
EBMR (Evidence-Based Medicine Reviews) is a database of evidence-based medical interventions.

59. **C) One indirect cost 2-hour training session offered both in-person and online with a nutritionist and staff from a local relocation agency, to be offered twice over the course of a semester (Area VIII)**
Providing the flexibility of in-person or online training opens the doors for more people to attend, as does repeating the training twice in the semester. Combining presentations on the topic and addressing the audience's needs should help prepare staff most appropriately.

60. **B) Secondary (Area II)**
Secondary audiences are those who can help reach or influence the intended or primary audience (in this case, the men in need of primary care).

61. **A) In-person interview (Area I)**
In-person interviews are very costly to conduct because they are very labor intensive.

62. **D) Attitude (Area VIII)**
In the Theory of Planned Behavior, the construct of "attitude" refers to the degree to which a person has a favorable or unfavorable evaluation of the behavior of interest, including a consideration of the outcomes of performing the behavior. Because the woman strongly believes she will gain weight if she quits smoking, this represents an attitude toward quitting smoking.

63. **A) Share the results at community meetings and with local stakeholders (Area IV)**
The sixth and final step in the Centers for Disease Control and Prevention (CDC) Evaluation Framework is "Use and Share Lessons Learned." At the end of a program, you need to disseminate your work as broadly as possible. While that may involve writing a report to the funder, that should not be the extent of your dissemination. In this case, local stakeholders must be engaged to attend to the local needs.

64. **A) Health education (Area I)**
Health problems that are highly changeable and highly important to the population are likely to be influenced through an educational approach.

65. **D) Gantt chart (Area III)**
A Gantt chart is a visual diagram that depicts the tasks, person assigned to tasks, effort, and timeline for implementation of program activities.

66. **B) Comprehensiveness (Area VIII)**
Social marketing has clearly defined behavioral goals and focuses on those goals specifically. Programs do need to be cost-effective, thoroughly informed by market research, and always recognize competition.

67. **A) Face-to-face meetings (Area V)**
Studies have shown that, of the above choices, personal contact is the best facilitated use of information by policy makers.

68. **B) Sense of mission (Area VII)**
Understanding the mission, vision, values, beliefs, and ethics of an organization is to exhibit a sense of the mission of an organization. It does not necessarily imply that one has leadership skills or political competencies, but can articulate the core principles and philosophies of the organization.

69. **C) In-kind donations (Area VII)**
In-kind donations are something you would list on a grant budget but not an operating budget, which generally focuses on revenue and costs.

70. **D) A and B (Area IV)**
A data analysis and reporting plan would never a priori presume any findings.

71. **A) Education (Area III)**
In a novel situation where most people are simply unaware of a risk and there are few barriers to performing a behavior (in this case, not playing a game while driving), education is likely the easiest, least expensive, and thus the first choice of intervention.

72. **D) Legislation (Area III)**
When education and persuasive techniques have failed to bring about the desired levels of behavior change, legal solutions are often employed.

73. **D) Who is having this problem? (Area V)**
A key first step in developing advocacy plans is identifying who is affected by a particular social or policy issue.

74. **B) Media advocacy (Area V)**
Media advocacy is when individuals or organizations use the media (traditional or online) for advocacy purposes.

75. **C) The drop in standardized test scores following the outbreak (Area V)**
Policy makers are likely to be influenced by local data and information, especially when linked to tangible outcomes of public interest. Fact sheets should be kept to one page andx include easy-to-read information that describes local data in context to state or national data.

76. **C) Key informant (Area I)**
A key informant interview is a qualitative, in-depth interview with people who have expertise or know what is going on in the community around a specific health topic or problem area.

77. **B) Measurable (Area II)**
Objectives must be measurable to quantify or measure progress.

78. **C) Product, price, place, and promotion (Area VII)**
The *product* (tangible or intangible) satisfies the consumer's needs or wants, the *price* is what the customer pays (in direct or indirect costs), the *place* is where the customer accesses the product, and the *promotion* is the marketing communication.

79. **C) Innovators (Area VIII)**
Innovators are the very first to adopt a behavior. Early adopters are next.

80. **A) Talk to students about their health concerns (Area I)**
Assessing needs with the target population is an important first step in program planning.

81. **A) Consulting (Area VI)**

82. **C) Health Belief Model (Area VIII)**
"Perceived susceptibility" is another way of saying "perceived threat of a disease," a core construct of the Health Belief Model.

83. **B) Outside your control (Area II)**
Strengths and weaknesses are within the organization's control. Opportunities and threats are outside the organization's control.

84. **A) Program planning (Area II)**
Program planning involves identifying the needs, priorities, and potential causes of health problems, as well as facilitators and barriers to achieving the overall objectives and goals of a program.

85. **D) Determine the objectives of the focus group> Determine the focus group questions to be asked> Determine a data analysis plan> Recruit participants (Area I)**
Qualitative data are collected methodically, just as quantitative data are. First, the objectives of the study are determined. Then questions would be created to capture the data needed to satisfy project objectives. Next, a data analysis plan would be constructed to ensure that the data could be obtained from the questions asked, along with the methods for doing so (number of coders, method of coding, etc.). Only after that would recruitment of participations begin.

86. **C) Geographical limitations (Area I)**
Conducting surveys remotely can eliminate or reduce geographical limitations to research.

87. **D) Even if you design, recruit, and analyze your focus groups well, you may need additional needs assessment information (Area I)**
Focus groups can provide rich and deep information, but they should not be considered the sole source of information because they are not representative. Individual focus groups generally should be homogeneous to facilitate honest opinion sharing. In this case, mixing management and labor might constrain employees' willingness to share their opinions.

88. **B) Nominal (Area IV)**
Nominal data can also be thought of as "named" data ("red, blue, green" or "high, medium, low").

89. **B) Memorandum of Understanding (MOU) (Area V)**
An MOU is a more informal document than an MOA, which can have legal implications.

90. **D) Exposure to toxic substances (Area III)**
Exposure to toxic substance is a biologic factor, though may be influenced by things like poverty, poor housing, and so on, which would be addressed in the Social Ecological Model.

91. **B) Teaching strategies (Area VI)**
    Varying teaching strategies can make sure you are addressing the needs of different types of learners.

92. **C) Change in knowledge (Area V)**
    Pretest–posttest evaluation is best suited to detect a change in something, such as knowledge, attitude, or skill. It can also measure changes in behavioral intention.

93. **A) Assessing existing health needs and problems (Area II)**
    Planning begins with assessing the situation and identifying the health problems that are occurring.

94. **A) Process evaluation (Area IV)**
    A process evaluation focused on program fidelity or the extent to which a program is being implemented as it was designed and planned, including program inputs, outputs, activities, and overall implementation.

95. **B) Change of attitude, acquisition of skills, short-term retention of information, long-term retention of information, decision-making, reinforcement of behavior, maintenance of behavior (Area III)**
    The Hierarchy of Effects Model describes the process people go through as they decide to buy goods or adopt behaviors.

96. **B) Randomization (Area IV)**
    Quasi-experimental differs from experimental research in that there is no randomization in terms of who is assigned to the control and treatment groups.

97. **C) Needs assessment data (Area II)**
    Ideally, the needs assessment should drive the development of the goals and objectives for the program. BRFSS data are a valuable source of population-level data but cannot provide specifics about conditions faced by the local nonprofit or their clients or partners. Finally, while other's evaluation data can be useful to help inform your project, it should not dominate your thinking.

98. **C) Valid (Area I)**
    Valid measures measure what they are supposed to—if you get on a scale, it will tell you what you actually weigh. Reliable measures will work each time.

99. **D) Correlation (Area IV)**
    Correlation cannot imply causation.

100. **C) Mixed methods (Area I)**
    A mixed-methods approach can provide program planners with a balance between the efficiency and generalizability of quantitative methods, such as surveys, by balancing out their limitations of lack of context and shallowness of the data by supplementing them with qualitative methods such as interviews and focus groups to gain richer, deeper understanding of participant needs and perspectives. These relatively more expensive and less generalizable methods can be used where needed as either exploration to inform the development of the quantitative work or to further explore themes found in the quantitative needs assessment that program planners do not understand and need more information about to move forward.

101. **D) Capricious (Area VI)**
Health communication materials should always be clear, credible, and consistent. Capriciousness, or being given to sudden and unaccountable changes of mood or behavior, is not a desirable quality in health communication materials.

102. **A) The costs of training volunteers to transport participants in such a way as to satisfy liability concerns (Area III)**
Using volunteers to transport participants might incur significant costs to receive certifications to satisfy insurance and other legal or regulatory agencies. Training costs can be a significant barrier for implementation of programs.

103. **C) Employee leisure-time activities (Area IV)**
While employee leisure-time activities do contribute significantly to overall health and well-being, they are outside of the control of an employer and a worksite health promotion program.

104. **A) Social determinates of health (Area VIII)**
Social determinates of health broadly affect peoples' health and contribute widely to disparities and inequities.

105. **B) In-depth interviews (Area I)**
In-depth interviews, participant observations, and focus group data are all examples of qualitative data.

106. **C) Innate, intrapersonal, interpersonal, institutional, community, public policy (Area III)**
The Social Ecological Model sees health as being influenced by a series of interconnected systems. The innate are those biologic factors a person is born with. The intrapersonal are an individual's knowledge, attitudes, behaviors, skills, and so on. Intrapersonal processes and primary groups are the formal and informal social networks and support systems surrounding the individual, such as families, work, and friendship networks. The next larger circle are institutional factors, such as social institutions and organizations, including formal and informal rules and regulations. Next, community factors, including relationships among organizations, institutions, and informal networks. Finally, the outermost circle, furthest from the individual on the model, are public policy, including laws and policies.

107. **D) Randomized control study (Area IV)**
Randomized controlled trials (RCTs) are considered the "gold standard" of causational studies.

108. **B) Social Ecological Model (Area VIII)**
The Social Ecological Model has four stages—the Individual, Interpersonal Relationships, Community, and Society.

109. **B) Young men who have been convicted of driving under the influence (DUI) (Area III)**
Young men who have been convicted of a DUI are the target audience for the intervention and thus have valuable insight into the causes of the problem and the needs of the audience.

110. **D) Interactions (Area III)**
The model is predicated on the idea that multiple levels of the model interact with each other.

111. **A) Extending personal invitations through staff, stakeholders, or clients (Area V)**
Expanding a volunteer network through those already involved with your organization is likely to be the most effective method of recruitment because it leverages existing relationships. Personalized requests are more likely to be responded to than mass requests, such as those over social or mass media.

112. **D) Social marketing (Area VII)**
Social marketing is concerned with increasing acceptability of a social idea through traditional marketing practices. This includes some of the "four Ps": product, price, place, and promotion.

113. **B) Primary (Area I)**
Primary research is new research that has been carried out to answer a specific question or set of questions.

114. **B) Convene a steering committee (Area VII)**
Since it is a community group, the health educator might select Mobilizing for Action through Planning and Partnerships MAPP to guide their efforts. Step one is "Partnership Development" so developing a steering committee is a good first step.

115. **C) Tailored (Area III)**
Tailored health communications have been shown to be effective in a variety of situations but are more expensive to produce and maintain.

116. **D) 12 months (Area II)**
A national health communication campaign can easily take a year or better to plan, including developing and testing materials.

117. **A) The program's activities and outputs (Area IV)**
Process indicators measure the programs outputs—whether program activities have been implemented as intended. Examples include: how many classes were held, how many posters were displayed, social media ads were run?

118. **B) Second-person language (Area V)**
The audience for a press release are the members of the media. Therefore, they are written in professional, third-person language.

119. **B) Coalition (Area V)**
Coalitions are structures of collaboration between groups or organizations, in which each group retains its identity, but all agree to work together toward mutually agreed-upon goals.

120. **A) Conduct a community analysis (Area I)**
Begin with an analysis of the situation facing the community to determine what needs the community faces. You cannot understand reinforcing factors until you have determined a particular health problem. You do not know which segment of the population's health literacy to investigate until you have determined which subsegments to address. And you cannot write a budget until much later in the planning process.

121. **A) Technical assistance (Area VII)**
Technical assistance is the process of providing targeted support to an organization with a development need or problem. It is an effective method for building the capacity of an organization.

122. **B) Make sure everyone in the group speaks (Area V)**
Usually it is best to identify one or two people to speak on behalf of the group. Meetings with legislators are usually short and limiting the number of people who speak keeps the meeting on track and keeps your message consistent.

123. **C) Interviews (Area VI)**
Interviews are usually examples of primary data.

124. **D) Cohort (Area III)**
A **cohort study** is a longitudinal study selected from a cohort (sharing a defining characteristic, such as birth or graduation), performing a cross-sectional studies at intervals through time.

125. **C) 40% (Area VI)**
Studies show that about 40% of Americans have inadequate levels of health literacy, and only 12% are in the "proficient" category.

126. **D) Behavioral Risk Factor Surveillance System (BRFSS) (Area I)**
Observations, focus groups, and diary reviews provide direct information about the behavior of individuals and groups, permit evaluators to enter into and understand the situation and/or context, and provide opportunities for identifying unanticipated outcomes. These are all hallmarks of qualitative data.

127. **D) Describe how they will measure variables in program (Area II)**
The methods section is the place to describe how variables will be measured in the project.

128. **A) Emphasize the instructor's education and experience (Area VI)**
When an audience is reluctant, making the information relevant to them is especially important. Stress what value the new information brings to their lives: Does it make their job easier to perform? Does it make their children healthier? What does it get them that they want?

129. **B) Find out more about the audience (Area VI)**
Understanding the audience to whom he will be presenting will be critical. Some questions he might want to ask are: How many people will be there? Were they involved in the assessment? Are they receptive or hostile to the findings? How long will they plan on staying? Have they been to a meeting like this before? What are they expecting him to say? What questions do they have? What style of presentation should he use? Should he use PowerPoint?

130. **A) Learning objective (Area III)**
Learning objectives are important because they give students a sense of what to expect in a course and guide the instructor's assessment strategies.

131. **C) Pilot project (Area III)**
A pilot is a trial of an intervention in its entirety run in a limited location. The results are used to fix problems and make changes before a full-scale project implementation.

132. **B) Grassroots advocacy/direct advocacy (Area VII)**
Grassroots advocacy harnesses the power of the public to bring pressure upon elected officials to make policy changes, as opposed to direct advocacy, or lobbying, which relies on paid or volunteer staff to lobby officials for change.

133. **C) Justify (Area II)**
"List" comes from the "Remembering" or lowest domain. "Use" comes from the "Applying" or third domain. "Analyze" comes from the "Analyzing" or fourth domain. "Justify" comes from the "Evaluating" or fifth domain.

134. **A) A theory is more likely to be tested and proven by research (Area VIII)**
**Theory** is defined as a set of concepts, definitions, and propositions that explain or predict events or situations by illustrating the relationships between variables. Theories should be applicable to a broad variety of situations. A theory presents a systematic way of understanding events or situations. Theories are usually more likely to have been tested by research while models may draw on a number of theories but are not always as specified as a theory and many have not been highlight developed or rigorously tested.

135. **B) Process, outcome, impact (Area IV)**
Most program evaluations will investigate process, outcome, and impact evaluation, though some will be limited to one or two of the above (i.e., merely a process evaluation)

136. **D) Done it and taught it to someone else (Area II)**
The old adage from medical school is when you are learning something you "see one, do one, teach one." Practicing a skill and teaching it to someone else under supervised conditions is a most effective way of learning information.

137. **C) Sharing and validating the needs that have been identified (Area I)**
Validating the results of your needs assessment with the community will confirm that the priorities the needs assessment has identified are appropriate and acceptable to the community.

138. **B) Create a community advisory board to inform organizational activities (Area VIII)**
Partnering with the community, perhaps through the creation of an advisory board, could help the organization better understand how to offer effective, equitable, and respectful quality services.

139. **D) Is the information written in an active or passive voice? (Area VI)**
While active voice is preferred for readability, it is not important for assessing the quality of online information. In this case, questions like the source of the information, are sources and citations offered, and is there a date that the site was last updated are more imported for assessing the quality of the website.

140. **B) The use of structured questionnaires used to generate consensus in a group of experts (Area I)**
A Delphi method is a small-group research technique that seeks a consensus among experts through sequential rounds of data collection and reduction.

141. **B) TV (Area III)**
Because of its ubiquity and that TV is an audiovisual news source, it is the choice for people with low literacy levels.

142. **A) Pilot test (Area III)**
A pilot test would test just the materials for a project. The pilot project would test the entire implementation in a small geographical area.

143. **A) 18 to 29 (Area VI)**
Younger people are more likely than older people to use the internet, according to the Pew Internet and American Life Study. Ninety-nine percent of those 18 to 29 use the internet, 98% of those 30 to 49, 96% of those 50 to 64, and 75% of those 65+.

144. **C) Launch a pilot project in one neighborhood (Area II)**
Holding more focus groups is unlikely to turn up new data—she has reached saturation on this point. It is also unlikely she has reached the point in a program where she has held several focus groups and developed a program to this extent without having conducted a literature search on safe sleep. And given that the community has clearly expressed a need and desire, focusing on something else is not an acceptable choice. She is ready to launch a pilot project and see what opportunities and challenges exist when implementing the project.

145. **C) What will solve the problem? (Area I)**
The Epidemiological Model for needs assessment focuses on identifying problems, not identifying solutions.

146. **D) CINAHL (Area I)**
CINAHL (Cumulative Index to Nursing and Allied Health Literature) is the database for nursing and allied health professionals. NHANES (National Health and Nutrition Examination Survey), BRFSS (Behavioral Risk Factor Surveillance System), and MMWR (Morbidity and Mortality Weekly Report) are common sources of secondary data.

147. **B) If students will be embarrassed by the curriculum (Area I)**
     In considering a school-based curriculum, a school board would want to investigate cost, parental support (because parents could be a substantial roadblock to a sexual health curriculum being implemented in schools), and gather feedback about other users' experiences of other existing curricula. While the student experience is important, some embarrassment in discussing this topic in school is less concerning than the curriculum being evidence-based, acceptable to the community at large, affordable, and implemented appropriately.

148. **B) Avoid repetition (Area II)**
     Rather than avoiding repetition, the instructor should repeat key information, in interesting ways, throughout the instruction. Most people need to encounter new information more than once and in a variety of ways before they fully take in new information, especially if it is complex or particularly unfamiliar. Put another way, "practice makes perfect."

149. **D) Cross-sectional (Area III)**
     Cross-sectional studies are onetime studies that give researchers a "snapshot" of what is going on at a particular point in time. They are useful for determining prevalence of a health problem, among other things.

150. **A) A teachable moment (Area V)**
     Teachable moments are periods in time when events lend themselves to provide illustrations of concepts taught in educational materials. They can also be opportunities (from a SWOT analysis) or external, positive events for a campaign—moments that support the objectives of your campaign within the context of your community or give rise to the need for your campaign.

151. **A) Behavioral objective (Area II)**
     Behavioral objectives give the learner a sense of what specifically they will be able to do after completing the course.

152. **A) External (Area IV)**
     External validity has to do with how generalizable or applicable findings are to other populations, settings, and contexts.

153. **D) B and C (Area VI)**
     Practicing the presentation beforehand ensures that you are comfortable delivering the presentation and that your talk can be delivered in the appropriate amount of time. Limiting the text on the slide to only the key concepts helps make sure that it is readable to as wide an audience as possible and that the key concepts are remembered by the audience. A lot of animations can be distracting and may not be appropriate depending on the topic and audience.

154. **C) Former employees (Area I)**
     While former employees might have some valuable insights, it is current employees that are the audience of a worksite health promotion program. Given an unlimited budget and time frame, it might be worth speaking to former employees to see if they had left the company due to a lack of health services, but from a realistic standpoint, it make much more sense to focus resources on speaking to current employees, management, and those in the human resources department.

155. **D) Pretest–posttest design (Area III)**
Cross-sectional, cohort, and case control all help researchers describe or observe what is going on in various populations, but researchers do not try to change what is being experienced by those populations in the course of conducting the research. In experimental designs, such as randomized controlled trials (RCTs) or a pretest–posttest quasi-experimental design, researchers are trying to effect change in the study population.

156. **D) Environmental (Area II)**
Changes to the physical workplace constitute environmental changes.

157. **D) Coercive (Area V)**
Incentives must not be so economically motivating that they persuade people to do things they would not have otherwise agreed to do. In this situation, parents might choose to vaccinate their children, or say that they have, just to get the incentive.

158. **C) Draft a brochure and then get feedback from patients at the clinic (Area III)**
Because the mothers at the clinic have special characteristics (i.e., many did not graduate from high school, which makes them different from the general population), it would be best to create and test materials with this population to ensure the materials are a good fit for their needs. The patients at the clinic are the true experts as to their needs and desires for materials.

159. **A) Biologic factors such as genetics (Area I)**
Biologic factors are the least able to be influenced by health education. Health education is much more able to influence psychosocial and behavioral factors, and can influence people's responses to, and mitigation of, environmental factors.

160. **B) Overuse of ED services (Area VI)**
Patients with low health literacy are more likely to use the ED, have medication errors, and cost the healthcare system billions of dollars in excess funds each year.

161. **B) Adequate funding (Area III)**
In this case, the instructor simply needs adequate funding. With adequate funding, they can develop a program that fits the needs of the seniors. It is premature at this stage of program development to speculate whether dance classes or an e-learning facility (or any other particular intervention) will be appropriate.

162. **A) Chinese, French, Tagalog (Area VI)**
According to Hernandez, Dietrich, & Bauman (2022), the five most frequently spoken languages in the United States are (a) English, (b) Spanish, (c) Chinese, (d) French, and (e) Tagalog.

163. **B) Marketing plan (Area III)**
A marketing plan involves developing and implementing a communication strategy that reaches target audiences with planned messages or media.

164. **D) The medium and long-term outcomes are not plausible (Area IV)**

In this case, the long-term objective, "parents use new parenting skills," is a behavioral objective that the reduction in morbidity, "rates of child abuse are reduced," is predicated upon. Thus, the logical flow of the model is backward.

165. **D) The relevance of the information to the intended audience (Area VI)**

When evaluating websites, accuracy, relevance, and appropriateness to the intended audience are among the most important features to look for. Others include a clear understanding of who the author is and when the last time the site was updated.

## Table 11.1 Evaluation of Results

| Area of Responsibility | Question Numbers | Number of Questions | Number Correct | Percentage Correct | Topics Requiring Further Study? |
|---|---|---|---|---|---|
| 1. Area I: Assessment of Needs and Capacity | 1, 2, 3, 10, 21, 34, 35, 36, 61, 64, 76, 80, 85, 86, 87, 98, 100, 105, 113, 120, 126, 137, 140, 145, 146, 147, 154, 159 | 28 | __/28 | % | |
| 2. Area II: Planning | 5, 15, 17, 18, 22, 27, 32, 41, 54, 57, 60, 77, 83, 84, 93, 97, 116, 127, 133, 136, 144, 148, 151, 156 | 23 | __/23 | % | |
| 3. Area III: Implementation | 13, 38, 55, 56, 65, 71, 72, 90, 95, 102, 106, 109, 110, 115, 124, 130, 131, 141, 142, 149, 155, 158, 161, 163 | 24 | __/24 | % | |
| 4. Area IV: Evaluation and Research | 6, 20, 25, 26, 37, 42, 52, 58, 63, 70, 88, 94, 96, 99, 103, 107, 117, 135, 152, 164 | 20 | __/20 | % | |
| 5. Area V: Advocacy | 4, 28, 29, 31, 40, 43, 46, 50, 67, 73, 74, 75, 92, 111, 118, 119, 122, 132, 150, 157 | 20 | __/20 | % | |
| 6. Area VI: Communication | 11, 16, 39, 45, 47, 48, 49, 51, 78, 91, 101, 112, 125, 129, 139, 143, 153, 160, 162, 165 | 20 | __/20 | % | |
| 7. Area VII: Leadership and Management | 7, 8, 12, 68, 69, 89, 114, 121, 123, 128 | 10 | __/10 | % | |
| 8. Area VIII: Ethics and Professionalism | 9, 14, 19, 23, 24, 30, 33, 44, 53, 59, 62, 66, 78, 79, 81, 82, 104, 108, 134, 138 | 20 | __/20 | % | |

# So Now You Are a CHES®: What Is Next? Career Opportunities, Continuing Education, and Thinking About the MCHES® Certification

## ▶ CAREER OPPORTUNITIES FOR HEALTH EDUCATORS

Congratulations! Once you have passed the Certified Health Education Specialist (CHES®) exam, you will probably be looking for a job in which to use your health education skills. Fortunately, health educators are in demand in a variety of work settings. But where and how should you look for a job as a health educator?

## ▶ WHAT HEALTH EDUCATORS DO

Health educators teach people about behaviors that prevent illness or injury and promote wellness. They develop and implement strategies to improve the health of individuals and communities.

Health educators typically do the following:

- Provide needs assessment in workplaces, organizations, and communities.
- Develop programs to educate people about health topics or train them in skills needed to maintain health.
- Teach people how to manage health conditions.
- Evaluate the effectiveness of programs and educational materials.
- Help people find health services or information.
- Provide training programs for other health professionals.
- Supervise staff who implement health education programs.
- Collect and analyze data to learn about their audience and improve programs and services.
- Advocate for improved health resources and policies that promote health.

The duties of health educators depend on the work setting. You most likely will work in healthcare facilities, colleges, public health departments, nonprofits, and private businesses. Some CHES® work in secondary school settings as teachers, though usually with additional training or certification. What follows are some of the most common settings in which CHES®

may work, a description of the type of work they might do there, and resources for looking for employment in each setting.

## HEALTHCARE SETTING

In healthcare facilities, health educators may work one-on-one with patients and their families, or work with other healthcare professionals to improve the care patients receive. They teach patients about their diagnoses and about any necessary treatments or procedures. CHES® may work as patient navigators, helping consumers determine their health insurance options and directing people to outside resources, such as support groups and home health agencies. Health educators in healthcare facilities also help organize health fairs and classes. Professionally, CHES® can collaborate with other health professionals to ensure that health education classes and materials are understandable, culturally appropriate, and easily accessed by patients. Health educators may also be coaches and help patients lose weight, manage chronic disease, or quit smoking.

Salary for health educators ranges depending on region of the country, education, experience, and setting of the job. According to the Bureau of Labor Statistics (BLS), health educator jobs in hospital (government, state, local) settings are the highest paid, with a median salary of $65,530. Salaries for health educators who work in individual and family services are about one-third lower, with a median salary of $43,400. In September 2021, about a quarter of all health educators (24%) worked for the government, and 21% in healthcare settings.

## COLLEGE SETTING

In colleges, health educators create programs and materials on topics that affect young adults, such as sexual health, substance abuse, stress, and sleep. They employ a variety of methods and channels, including health fairs, dining hall nutrition trainings, and social media to make sure students are getting necessary health information. Health educators also advocate for campus policies to promote health, train resident assistants and peer health educators, and liaison with faculty and staff.

## FEDERAL, STATE, OR LOCAL PUBLIC HEALTH DEPARTMENT SETTING

In public health departments, health educators administer public health campaigns on topics such as emergency preparedness, immunizations, proper nutrition, and stress management. They develop materials to be used by other public health officials. During emergencies, they may provide safety information to the public and the media (as we have seen since the advent of COVID-19!). Some health educators work with other professionals to create public policies that support healthy behaviors and environments. They may also oversee grants and grant-funded programs to improve the health of the public. Some participate in statewide and local committees dealing with topics such as aging or environmental lead mitigation.

According to BLS, 24% of health educators were employed in a government setting. As of September 2021, salaries averaged $59,070, though there was a considerable range. Jobs at the local level may pay less than those at the state or national level.

## NONPROFIT OR COMMUNITY-BASED ORGANIZATION SETTING

In nonprofits (including community health organizations), health educators create programs and materials about health issues for the community their organization serves. They help organizations obtain funding and other resources. Many nonprofits focus on a particular disease or audience, so health educators in these organizations limit programs to that specific topic or audience. For example, a health educator may design a program to teach people with diabetes how to better manage their condition, or a program for teen mothers on how to care for their newborns. In addition, health educators may educate policymakers about ways to improve public health and work on securing grant funding for programs to promote health and disease awareness. Community-based organizations are often uniquely poised to rapidly respond to specific needs to communities because they are deeply rooted and have a deep understanding of local conditions.

While the BLS categorizes things a bit differently, approximately 20% of health education jobs are located in this category. Perhaps not surprisingly, wages are lower in these jobs. According to BLS (September 2021), jobs in the "religious, grantmaking, civic, professional, and similar organizations" category had a median salary of $49,090; those in the "individual and family services" category were the lowest, at a $43,040 median.

## WORKPLACE SETTING

The workplace is an important setting for health protection, health promotion, and disease prevention programs. On average, Americans who work full-time spend nearly half their waking hours at the workplace.

In private businesses, health educators identify common health problems among employees and create programs to improve health. They work with management to develop incentives for employees to adopt healthy behaviors, such as losing weight or controlling cholesterol. Health educators recommend changes to the workplace, such as creating smoke-free areas, to improve employee health.

### Salary Outlook

The median annual wage for health educators was $56,500 in May 2020. An occupation's median wage is the amount at which half its workers earned more and half earned less. In May 2020, the lowest 10% earned less than $33,720; the highest 10% earned more than $101,890 (Table 11.1).

**Table 12.1 Salary outlook**

| | |
|---|---|
| Hospitals: state, local, and private | $65,530 |
| Government | $59,070 |
| Outpatient health centers | $57,850 |
| Religious, grantmaking, civic, professional, and similar organizations | $49,090 |
| Individual and family services | $43,040 |

*Source*: www.bls.gov/ooh/community-and-social-service/health-educators.htm#tab-5.

# ▶ LOOKING FOR A JOB IN HEALTH EDUCATION

You are not alone when you are looking for a job in health education! There are a number of resources to use when looking for a job in health education. First, your school likely has a career services office that will have resources specific to public health and health education jobs. It can be very fruitful to utilize an alumni contact list, particularly if the alumni's CHES® status is available. Many CHES® find jobs through other CHES®, and it has been our experience that CHES® are happy to help fellow CHES® with job search advice, contacts, and experience.

The following is a list of public health- and health education-specific websites that frequently post the kinds of jobs for which CHES® are qualified:

## PUBLIC HEALTH JOB SEARCH ENGINES

- American Public Health Association Career Mart (http://careers.apha.org)
- Association of Schools and Programs of Public Health Careers (ASPPH; www.publichealt hjobs.org)
- Public Health Employment Connection (https://apps.sph.emory.edu/PHEC/)

## LOCAL AND STATE HEALTH DEPARTMENTS

- Allegheny County Health Department (alleghenycounty.us/Health-Department/ Resources/Careers/Careers.aspx)
- Association of State and Territorial Health Officials (www.astho.org/Careers-at-ASTHO)
- Maryland Department of Health and Mental Hygiene (www.jobaps.com/md/jobs/ dhmh)
- National Association of County and City Health Officials (NACCHO; careers.naccho. org/jobs)
- New York State Department of Health (www.health.ny.gov/employment/entry.htm)
- NYC Department of Health and Mental Hygiene (www.nyc.gov/careers)
- PA Department of Health (health.pa.gov/topics/Administrative/Pages/Jobs.aspx)
  *Also see state and local health department jobs on* governmentjobs.com *(use filters for Health Services>Public Health)*

## ACADEMIC OPPORTUNITIES AT SCHOOLS OF PUBLIC HEALTH

- Academic Keys for Health Sciences (healthsciences.academickeys.com/seeker_job.php)
- AcademyHealth (jobs.academyhealth.org)
- ChronicleVitae (Chronicle of Higher Education; chroniclevitae.com/job_search/new)
- HigherEd 360 (www.highered360.com/jobs)
- Higher Ed Jobs (www.higheredjobs.com)
- If you are seeking a research or faculty position at a school of public health, please visit the Association of Schools and Programs of Public Health (ASPPH) website (www.aspph. org) for member schools.

## GOVERNMENT OPPORTUNITIES

- All Federal Jobs (www.usajobs.gov)
- Centers for Disease Control and Prevention (CDC; jobs.cdc.gov)
- Centers for Medicare and Medicaid Services (CMS; cms.gov/About-CMS/ Career-Information/CareersatCMS)
- Council of State and Territorial Epidemiologists (CSTE) (jobs.cste.org)
- National Institute on Aging (www.nia.nih.gov/about/careers)
- National Institutes of Health (www.jobs.nih.gov)
- ORISE Fellowships and Research Opportunities with the CDC, U.S. Food and Drug Administration (FDA), U.S. Environmental Protection Agency (EPA), and so on (https:// bit.ly/39vBcrx)
- ORISE CDC Research Opportunities (https://orise.orau.gov/cdc/applicants/ current-research-opportunities.aspx)
- Pennsylvania Civil Service (https://www.employment.pa.gov/Pages/default.aspx)
- U.S. Agency for International Development (USAID; www.usaid.gov/careers and https://bit.ly/2JmPUqb)
- U.S. Department of Health and Human Services (www.hhs.gov/careers)
- U.S. EPA (www.epa.gov/careers)
- U.S. FDA (www.fda.gov/about-fda/jobs-and-training-fda)
- U.S. Public Health Service Commissioned Corps (https://www.usphs.gov/)

## INTERNATIONAL OPPORTUNITIES

- AmeriCares—International and domestic careers/internships (https://www.americares. org/take-action/jobs/)
- CAMRIS (https://careers-camris.icims.com/)
- CARE (http://www.care.org/careers)
- Clinton Health Access Initiative (CHAI; https://www.clintonhealthaccess.org/ join-our-team/)
- Devex International Development (https://www.devex.com/jobs)
- EngenderHealth—International and domestic careers and internships (www. engenderhealth.org)
- FHI360 (www.fhi360.org/careers)
- Gates Foundation (www.gatesfoundation.org/Careers)
- Global Health Technical Professionals (GHTP)—contractor for USAID (https:// bit.ly/2w0qj3h)
- Global Jobs (https://globaljobs.org/)
- Global Health Corps (https://ghcorps.org/fellows/apply-to-be-a-fellow/)
- Pan American Health Organization (PAHO; https://www.paho.org/en/careers-paho)
- PATH (path.silkroad.com/epostings)

- Peace Corps (www.peacecorps.gov)
- Social Solutions, Inc. (contractor for USAID; https://jobs-socialsolutions.icims.com/jobs/intro)
- World Health Organization (WHO; www.who.int/careers/)

*For more ideas, see the Global Health Employers list under the "Careers" _section on the Pitt Public Health website.*

## GENERAL JOB SEARCH ENGINES

- Idealist (www.idealist.org)
- Indeed (www.indeed.com)
- Simply Hired (www.simplyhired.com)
- LinkedIn (Jobs-www.linkedin.com/jobs)

## SALARY INFORMATION

- Bureau of Labor Statistics (https://www.bls.gov/bls/blswage.htm)
- Glassdoor (https://www.glassdoor.com)
- LinkedIn Salary (www.linkedin.com/salary)
- Pay Scale (www.payscale.com)
- Salary.com (www.salary.com)

## ▶ MAINTAINING YOUR CERTIFICATION

Passing your test is not the last thing you have to do to be a CHES®. As soon as your certification arrives, you need to start thinking about *maintaining* your credentials. As of the writing of this book, the following information is correct, but always check with NCHEC for the latest requirements! In order to maintain certification, a CHES® must obtain a minimum of 75 Continuing Education Contact Hours (CECH) over the 5-year certification period. National Commission for Health Education Credentialing, Inc. (NCHEC) encourages all CHES® to accumulate a minimum of 15 CECH per year, and to complete all continuing education (CE) requirements at least *90 days* prior to recertification.

Within the 75 hours you must accumulate over the 5-year period, there are three types of credits you need.

The first type of credit is Category I hours, which are CE hours that have been preapproved by NCHEC. You must have at least 45 of these hours in each 5-year period, though you may earn more. Designated providers—schools, universities, conferences, health departments, and so on—have arrangements with NCHEC and provide it with specific information on their trainings, conferences, and so on. They then request approval for a certain number of Category 1 hours. One of the nice things about Category 1 hours is that they do not require much from you in the way of paperwork—when you attend the event, you provide the registrar with your CHES® number (you might want to save this as a note in your phone so you always have it) and the registrar submits the paperwork to NCHEC for you. Designated providers only have to submit to NCHEC quarterly (which is why NCHEC wants you to have all your hours completed 90 days before recertification is due). Many conferences, meetings, and classes have costs associated with them, but there are sources that offer Category 1 credits for no or very low cost.

Category II credits do not require preauthorization and can be claimed by submitting a Category 2 form from NCHEC's website. These credits can include things like attending a meeting for which no Category 1 credits were offered, creating a class or a training, authoring a journal article or a book, or presenting at a conference. Up to 30 Category 2 hours may be claimed in each 5-year cycle. If you reside outside of the United States, you may claim all 75 hours as Category 2 credits.

The third type of credit you need is called "Continuing Competency" credits. They are designed to demonstrate continued levels of knowledge, skills, and/or abilities for CHES® throughout their careers. They can be either Category I or Category II but they must contain some sort of evaluation with them. In the case of Category I credits, that involves some sort of quiz by the provider of the Category I credit. If you are using Category II credits, you will need your supervisor to provide an evaluation of your job duties. Either way, you will need to provide 5 of your 75 credits as these "Continuing Competency" credits, in any combination.

## ▶ QUESTIONS ABOUT CONTINUING EDUCATION

### YIKES! SEVENTY-FIVE IS A LOT OF HOURS. HOW DO I MANAGE?

NCHEC recommends that CHES® earn 15 hours a year, and submit their final hours at least 90 days before the end of the recertification cycle. By keeping up each year and spreading the 75 out over the 5-year period, it is not terribly burdensome and ensures that you are up-to-date as a practitioner. Think of it as keeping the oil changed in your car—it is just professional maintenance.

### HOW DO I KNOW IF SOMETHING IS A CATEGORY 1 OR CATEGORY 2 CREDIT?

Usually a training, conference, meeting, or some other approved activity, such as reading a journal article and taking a quiz, will be clearly designated as having Category 1 credits. It will say something like "'X activity' has been preapproved by NCHEC for 4.0 hours of continuing education," or "4.0 hours have been approved for CHES®." If claiming Category 2 credits, be sure to do so within 90 days of having completed the activity.

### MY JOB DOES NOT PAY FOR CONTINUING EDUCATION. WHERE CAN I FIND FREE OR LOW-COST CREDITS?

NCHEC does not charge processing fees to CHES® for CE hours, though many of the places that offer CE hours, such as conferences, do charge a fee. However, there are many opportunities for free or low-cost CE. The CDC offers many CHES® credits for free at www2a.cdc.gov/tceonline (you will have to create a log-in). NCHEC also maintains an extensive list of opportunities.

Many health departments or schools of public health may also offer free CHES® credits. One source of low-cost CHES® credits that we have used is www.healthedpartners.org/continuing_education.html. (DISCLOSURE: We received no compensation for this mention. We are simply fans.)

# ▶ OBTAINING THE ADVANCED-LEVEL CREDENTIAL (MASTER CERTIFIED HEALTH EDUCATION SPECIALIST)

Once you have served as a CHES® for at least 5 years, you may consider upgrading your credential to a Master Certified Health Education Specialist (MCHES®). MCHES® are much less numerous than CHES®–around 2,000–and in 2021 around 228 people registered to take the exam (https://www.nchec.org/overview). We will say it again, as of the writing of this book, the following information is correct, but always check with NCHEC for the latest information and requirements! According to NCHEC, an MCHES® is an advanced-level practitioner that has:

1. Met required academic qualifications
2. Worked in the field for a minimum of 5 years
3. Passed a competency-based examination administered by the NCHEC
4. Satisfied the CE requirement to maintain the national credential

Becoming an MCHES® takes additional time, energy, and work. You have to have been practicing as a health educator for at least 5 years in a paid capacity (volunteer time does not count). The 5 years of professional practice do not have to be consecutive years—part-time and nonconsecutive service counts. If you have been a CHES® for 5 years, you are qualified to take the exam. If you have not been a CHES® for 5 years but do have the required education AND 5 years of experience working as a health educator, you may qualify. There is a prescreening option if you are not sure you meet the academic requirements.

Just like the CHES® exam, the MCHES® examination is a criterion-referenced test that contains 165 multiple choice items; 150 of the items are used for the total score and there are 15 pilot items. The MCHES® examination is also available through computer testing at more than 400 testing sites worldwide.

The Eight Areas of Responsibility for Health Education Specialists[1] are the same for the MCHES®, but the percentage of questions for each responsibility differs. The following is the MCHES® examination blueprint based on the Health Educator Practice Analysis and the percentages of questions by the Eight Areas of Responsibility for Health Education Specialists (Table 11.2).

As you can see, the MCHES® exam focuses more on conducting evaluation and research related to health education/promotion and on administering and managing health education/promotion than does the CHES® exam.

**Table 12.2** MCHES® examination blueprint based on the Health Educator Practice Analysis and the percentages of questions by the Eight Areas of Responsibility for Health Education Specialists

| Area of Responsibility for Health Education Specialists | Percent of Questions on MCHES® Exam |
| --- | --- |
| Assessment of Needs and Capacity | 12 |
| Planning | 10 |
| Implementation | 9 |
| Evaluation and Research | 20 |
| Advocacy | 9 |
| Communications | 12 |
| Leadership and Management | 18 |
| Ethics and Professionalism | 10 |

---

[1] The Eight Areas of Responsibility for Health Education Specialists are copyright of the National Commission for Health Education Credentialing, Inc. (NCHEC).

# ▶ FINAL THOUGHTS

We hope this study guide has been helpful to you as you prepare for your CHES® exam. For us, being a CHES® and then MCHES® has been critical in our professional journeys. We believe it is a credential that demonstrates a commitment to health education, communication, equity, and service. We look forward to having you join the ranks of those who value the work of health educators. Truly, the future of the field has never looked better.

WELCOME TO THE RANKS OF CHES®!

# Index